Finding Perspective...

Raising Successful Children Affected by Fetal Alcohol Spectrum Disorder

A Parent's Guide to Creating Prevention
Strategies and Intervention Techniques Using
the OBD (Organic Brain Dysfunction)
3 Step Plan of Action!

By Liz Lawryk and Parents Everywhere

with contributions from

Ray Campbell, Juanita Carberry
Peggy Schlosser, Berna Stewa
Allison Waks and Dε

D1042726

Library and Archives Canada Cataloguing in Publication

Lawryk, Liz 1959 -

　　Finding Perspective... Raising Successful Children Affected by Fetal Alcohol Disorder / Liz Lawryk; edited by Jason Pohranychny ... [et al.].

Includes bibliographical references and index.

ISBN 0-9737739-0-1

　　1. Fetal alcohol syndrome. 2. Children of prenatal alcohol abuse--Care. 3. Children of prenatal alcohol abuse--Family relationships. 4. Parents of children with disabilities. I. Pohranychny, Jason, 1971- II. Title.

　　RG629.F45L39　　　2005　　　649'.151　　　C2005-903112-3

Edited by: Hazel Bergen, Emilia M. Dunphy, Henri Garand and Jason Pohranychny

Published by the OBD Triage Institute Inc.
P.O. Box 1289
Bragg Creek, Alberta, Canada
TOL OKO

Printed by Sundog Printing, Calgary, Alberta, Canada.

Contents

Chapter Five

Chapter Six

Chapter Seven

Chapter Eight

Chapter Nine

Chapter Ten

Chapter Eleven

Chapter Twelve

Chapter Thirteen

Families making it work . . .

Chapter Fourteen

Chapter Fifteen

In Closing

This book is dedicated to all the children, youth and families that I've met and have yet to meet.

From you we learn the most.

Foreward

Ray of hope

Success is not my own, I have to share it with those with whom I have walked this Journey...

My everyday life is not unlike your own. I eat and sleep just like the masses; I hurt, love, and laugh just like my neighbours; and I worry, obsess and wonder like other parents but with one encompassing difference - I sit in a boat with no directions to shore, no wind in my sails and a teacup for bailing, should I ever find the need to do so. The overcast is a constant and the ports of call do not speak my language. So, in a nutshell, I am lost without support.

Part of my "unsuccess," I believe, was due to the fact that everyone used to hold my hand and pull me to shore rather than guide me to where I needed to be. I was often over-helped. I, however, do not want to sound ungrateful. I just want to point out that helping is a bit like keeping the training wheels on a bicycle too long. Conversely, when I was encouraged to succeed and shown how to enjoy my successes big or little, it helped me to grow and do some of my own healing. Remember, there is a tremendous amount of misunderstanding about this disability, and sometimes I felt that I was made to be responsible for my situation.

I am almost forty years old and just learning that life can be fulfilling and interesting when given the tools to strive to be who I am, be that creative or cognate. Take care that you don't judge "me" at face value because I am much more than the "guy whose mother drank too much." I am Ray the father, the boyfriend, the best friend, an aspiring writer and a respected supervisor at my job. Please know: I am R-A-Y, not F-A-S.

Ray Campbell

Acknowledgements

I would like to extend my heartfelt gratitude to all of the families that I have worked, laughed and cried with over the years. I only wish I could name everyone, but the list is endless and I fear that I would leave someone out. You know who you are. Thank you for sharing your experiences with me in order to help so many other children and families. This has been a work in progress over several years, and for that, I would like to thank my family, friends and colleagues who have supported this project from its inception.

A big thanks and special credit to my Mom, Olga Fyfe, for giving me the ability to create and teach, and most importantly, for keeping me organized and having a sense of humour! To my family including Yvette Lawryk and Ed Barrette, Allison, Rachel, Melinda and Kevin Lawryk, The Stackiw, Lobas and O'Neil families, as well as Pam and Jonathan Legg, Carol, Don, Ali and Chris Soby, Jocelyn Horb and Val Robinson, to all, your patience and support has been much appreciated. My special thanks to Janet Wetter, Darren Big Crow, Susan Iuni, Hazel Bergen, Mandy, David, Lyndsay, Susan and JD Latiff, Michelle Peterson, Franceen Waxman, Austin and Sam Kombargi, Linda Falconberg, Carmen and David Esch. My sincere gratitude to Dr. Carey, Suzanne, Stephanie and Christine Johnson, Emilia, Jim, Stephen and Lee-Jay Dunphy, Charlaine, Jessica, Nicole and Tyler Mikuska and Paul and Kendra Baxter, the entire Bara family clan, Dr. Catherine Scotland, Deb Struiksma and Marilyn Casper, Dr. Linda Storoz, Donna Debolt, Mary Berube, Trina McFarlane, Dorothy Badry, Shirley Wormsbecker, Dr. Heidi-Marie Schroter, The Honourable Judge Bruce Fraser, Donna Anderson, Diane Wrubleski and all of the Calgary Joining Forces members, Constable Jim Olsen, Sharon and family, Lynette Wray, Daana Ormstrup, Colleen Burns, Gerry Cyr, Maralee Stewart and Diesel, Darren Joslin, Karl and

Christel Schunicht and family. Many thanks to Marie and Norm Brownell and the Alberta Foster Parents Association members, Lenora Thorkelson, Cindy Malazdrewicz, and Shauna Henderson, Joni Morrison-O'Hara, Ruth Copot, Hopeton, Lona, Sara, Anthony and Adrienne Louden, Dr. John Pearce and Dr. Terry Pezzot-Pearce, Candace Robb, Linda Simser, Wanda Riddell, Carly Burnett and Doug Darwish, Fay and Henri Garand ,Cathy and Jody McIssac, Nancy and Jim McPhee and family, the Wilson family, Konrad Dytnerski, The Honourable Iris Evans and Michelle Harder. Thanks to Dr. Colleen Klein, The Honourable Heather Forsyth, The Honourable Judge Ted Carruthers, The Honourable Judge Nancy Flatters for their continued support in our community. I am especially grateful to my good friend and colleague, Mr. Jason Pohranychny for his hard work and dedication to this book and to the FASD community, and a special hello to Kate-Lynn Pohranychny. My thanks to Dr. Susan Astley and Dr. Sterling Clarren, Sandra Clarren and Dan Dubovsky for getting us started. To Linda McRitchie, Cheryl Gross, Gail Henderson and Erma Bombeck wherever you are, thanks for the laughs and tremendous inspiration.

Last but not least, to Glenn Lawryk, who taught me to believe in myself and others, and who is truly, a really great sport.

Introduction

Fetal Alcohol Syndrome was medically labelled in North America in 1973, but the range of organic brain dysfunction, from moderate to severe, was not yet fully appreciated. Even by approximately 1989, a parent would say, "I think there is something wrong with our child, but no one seems to be able to give us any answers." Typically, these were loving, nurturing and resourceful parents who had taken their children to numerous professionals. Often the result was a host of diagnoses or, in some cases, suggestions that their parenting skills were to a degree at fault.

As a home visitor, I have had the opportunity to observe many children in their own environment, and I found myself asking parents how they had possibly managed to cope with the "crazy-making" behaviours that produced chronic and ever-present stress levels. Often this stress was undetected by family members themselves because all their energies focused on getting help for their child.

Then came the arrival of information sharing in the forms of literature, the Internet, videos, workshops, support groups and most fortunately, Diagnostic Clinics. The medical diagnostic terminology was updated from "Fetal Alcohol Syndrome" and "Fetal Alcohol Effect" to "Fetal Alcohol Spectrum Disorder," in recognition of the incredible range of variables within the disability. Nonetheless, in my work over the last ten years with families affected by alcohol-related disabilities, parents have consistently disclosed a new dilemma: "We had the label, but we never really knew exactly what it meant or what to do."

Since no two individuals are ever affected by prenatal alcohol exposure exactly the same way, the goal of this book is to provide specialized prevention techniques and intervention strategies designed for the patient's *unique abilities*, as opposed to a generalized FASD approach. Most of the ideas in this book have been long established in foundation and practice by the real experts - parents. In sharing their knowledge they are by far the largest contributors of hope for other families, as well as educators to the professionals and community members involved in supporting their objectives for their children.

The **OBD** 3 Step Plan of Action! addresses these issues by providing an easy-to-follow guide so that anyone can better understand a very complex medical diagnosis of organic brain dysfunction, and then construct and implement strategies based on factual information, not guesswork. Our intent is to identify and promote individual's strengths, while acknowledging and respecting their challenges. With this philosophy we aim to provide the best possible chance of future success for those affected and the families that care for them.

Chapter One

Once we heard the diagnosis

One of the roles in completing premedical assessments is to prepare parents for the possibility of a diagnosis of FASD. What I've learned over the years is that one can't. In participating in the evaluation process many parents indicated that they knew there would be a diagnosis established and would not be surprised. And then it happens. They get the diagnosis, see it in writing and feel as if they're going to fall apart. In a moment all of their hopes and dreams for their child are shattered: "I'd like to introduce our son the paediatrician who is also the starting quarterback this weekend and after the game will perform a one man musical and then go on to swim the English Channel." Other well-meaning people give advice like "Just get him through grade eight and try to keep him out of jail." Is it disheartening? You bet. Can we help? Absolutely.

As no two patients are ever affected the same way, the trick is to have an accurate explanation of *your child's* place within the incredibly wide spectrum of this disorder. By taking into account physiological differences, understanding cognitive or "thinking" abilities, and taking stock in your own expectations, you are then ready to start to take a fresh and promising direction. This is a disability that tends to provoke a range of behaviours, possibly for both of you. Please know that you are not alone and that parents whose child has had a recent diagnosis such as Obsessive Compulsive Disorder, Autism or Attention Deficit Hyperactivity Disorder often feel much the same way, as with these other medical diagnoses the behaviours are often very similar. All of these children, youth and adults need some help interpreting the world, and we need to understand how they see it. This is how you will make all the difference in raising a strong, successful child.

The "Label" and segregation

Over 25 years ago, as a student practicing at a Children's Hospital, my role was to assist families with the emotional ramifications of a recent medical diagnosis of their child, many with Down syndrome. In some cases, parents were told that their child would likely require a "special school" and "may need to be placed in a group home or institutional care." Back then we did not have accommodations for parents to stay overnight with sick kids like Ronald McDonald House, and organized support groups for parents were rare. It was the parents of these children that advocated for these services in order to provide essential, fair and progressive teaching and living practices, but more importantly, promise for their child's future.

Now all these years later, the same conversations with parents of an alcohol-affected child are strikingly similar to the ones with parents of a child diagnosed with Down syndrome back then. "We were told he will need a special school and possibly a group home for FASD kids." In this day and age as a society, we wouldn't dare discuss these options with parents of a child with a different medical issue that resulted in brain damage. In our desperation to initiate and accumulate services, we have created a dissimilar standard for children and families affected by alcohol-related brain injury, one of overt and public labelling that involves not only a medical circumstance but a social condition as well - alcoholism. Suggestions of considering a different court process for youth and adults identified within the spectrum poses an interesting legal question: Are we then going to have a different process for a person with diabetes or schizophrenia? Certainly

Persons with Disabilities require certain modifications to sentencing considering their overall functioning abilities, but this is also true with an individual that is found to be in the throws of addictions or deemed in the Intellectually Deficient range of functioning.

A diagnosis within FASD identifies to the world the confidential and personal struggles of two people: a child and his or her biological mother. In isolating them we not only disrespect them but inadvertently chastise and hold them out for public judgment. Many people have mothers who are alcoholics; however, they choose not to share this information with others. Moreover, not all individuals that were exposed to alcohol *in utero* are affected. When this disability is segregated, affected persons and their families lose the right to privacy. Perhaps in desperation to understand such a complicated brain dysfunction, we have become almost desensitized, which in turn has created a somewhat insensitive attitude towards women who have struggled with an addiction to alcohol. This is not to suggest that we completely eliminate "FASD" from our vocabularies; rather, it is a gentle reminder of the consequences of indiscriminate labelling and the implications of dividing children, youth and adults with a variety of abilities.

Since individuals with other types of brain injury may display similar behaviours, many of the prevention strategies and intervention techniques suggested here will prove effective not only for those diagnosed with FASD, but for children, youth or adults with a range of central nervous system dysfunction issues as well.

Societal stigma

Why is Fetal Alcohol Spectrum Disorder often not viewed as a medical disposition that results in disabilities, which in turn translate to behaviours? Unfortunately, the answer may lie in our society's predisposition to make assumptions based on physical appearance, a tendency amplified by various media including television, magazines, videos and movies. Stereotypes abound: blondes have more fun, a person wearing plain clothing is not wealthy, and let's not forget that you are not as attractive if you weigh over 92 pounds. Physical features that are specific to some alcohol-affected individuals (and others with syndromes similar in physical presentation) may, in fact, lead to erroneous conjecture regarding that person's abilities and even supposed intentions.

As a child I spent summers at my grandmother's house, and I recall a certain neighbourhood boy who had so much energy his nickname was "Lightning." He would run everywhere and do things impulsively without thinking. These were signs that Lightning likely had Attention Deficit Hyperactivity Disorder, just as his moniker suggested. The whispers in the community implied that his mother was "a drinker" and had no control over the actions of her child. In the weekly coffee klatch I would hear mutterings about Lightning: "I know he is a cheat because he has those small, beady eyes, his hair is always a mess because his mother doesn't look after him, his eyes are so far apart you would be crazy to trust him . . . you can tell he is not too smart by the way he talks." Years later, I bolted out of bed at three in the morning with a stunning revelation: Lightning seemed to have micropthmalia (small eyeballs), abnormal occipital hair whorls (hair grows in a target-like fashion, can be more than one and placed anywhere on the scalp), hypertelorism (eyes appear wide apart from each other) and speech articulation problems (not reflective of intelligence). He was probably an undiagnosed child of Fetal Alcohol Spectrum Disorder.

The moral of this story is that although acceptance of persons with differences has much improved since then, we need to make every effort to shield our kids from unnecessary ridicule and boost their self-esteem. As Kermit the frog once said, "It isn't easy being green." They have enough roadblocks in life possibly with learning or just fitting in, and these in many cases are further complicated by noticeable physical dissimilarities. If they have crooked teeth, get them braces; a wandering eye, get it corrected; speech problems, see a Speech and Language Specialist. Most provinces and states have disabilities and/or health care funding programs that might be able to provide financial assistance to mend them and get them off to a good, confident start.

Chapter Two

Terminology

Although perhaps somewhat intimidating, the more recent Diagnostic Terminology within the umbrella term of *Fetal Alcohol Spectrum Disorder* (FASD) is much more accurate than the previous terms, Fetal Alcohol Syndrome and Fetal Alcohol Effect. Prior to the amendment, there was often a misconception that "FAE was not as severe as FAS," which we clearly know today is not always the outcome.

Many patients previously diagnosed with FAE are at much greater risk for problems due to the "invisibility" of their disability. Since the facial features associated with FASD are predominantly developed in the first trimester, absence of dysmorphic facial features or evidence of mild facial markers does not always reflect the severity of the disability. With milder forms of dysfunction, the patient may be of average or above average intelligence, but may not have "common sense" or problem-solving abilities. Overall executive functioning refers to the abilities that underline independent, purposeful, contextually appropriate behaviour. This is clearly the essence of the disability.

By contrast, in severe cases, as with other forms of brain injury, the damage can be extreme: individuals can be rendered in a completely dependent state, unable to feed themselves, walk or communicate. For those patients with a static encephalopathy diagnosis (brain injury that is not progressive) we cannot heal their brains because the damage was done before birth, unlike for a stroke or car crash victim where in some cases the brain can be rehabilitated. The difference is that the latter brain was intact to begin with.

It is important to note that **only a medical doctor** trained in the evaluation of FASD is qualified to make a diagnosis. We would never label children with a diagnosis of diabetes without a full medical evaluation just because they are constantly urinating and tired. Some FASD patients have thin upper lips because their parents have thin upper lips. Facial features can be hereditary and require a specialist's examination. Further, many other syndromes mimic the physical, cognitive and behavioural presentation of Fetal Alcohol Syndrome, like Opitz Syndrome, Fragile X, Fetal Hydantoin (caused by the ingestion of anti-seizure medication in pregnancy), or a diagnosis such as Cornelia deLange, Noonan, Dubowitz or Aarskog syndromes, all requiring a genetics evaluation. For these reasons it is mandatory that all children, youth and adults are accurately pre-screened, evaluated and diagnosed by the appropriate medical professionals.

Physical and sensory abnormalities are common with prenatal alcohol exposure, so dental check-ups, hearing and vision testing are recommended. In some cases these may include Speech/Language Assessments and possibly speech therapy, occupational assessment/therapy and/or physiotherapy. For example, there is a higher incidence of strabismus (wandering or lazy eye) in this population of patients, and it is imperative that this is corrected prior to about age six, as after that approximate timeframe it is not fixable. (Doctors can attempt to straighten the muscles, but cannot correct the condition). For foster parents in particular, if this has not been done prior to the child or youth coming into your care, have it checked immediately. My friend Darren is 22 years of age and is having surgery to improve his severe strabismus. He is very much looking forward to the operation because the condition has always bothered him. This type of intervention is better late than never, as our ultimate goal is to build self-esteem at any stage for all children, youth and adults.

Physical anomalies that *translate* to the appearance of defiant behaviours

The following are illustrations of how physiological irregularities not only translate to seemingly wilful or oppositional behaviours, but may pose potential health risks. All too often, alcohol-affected persons are unintentionally reprimanded for behaviour that is a direct result of the unreliability of their physical composition. In the past, we seemed to have focused solely on how alcohol and other teratogens (anything that *adversely affects cellular development of the embryo or fetus)* have the potential to cause damage to the brain. Since our entire bodies are made up of cells, **any** part of the body could be compromised by the introduction of a teratogen during pregnancy. On further investigation, there is definitely a correlation between some *physical* anomalies and the appearance of defiant behaviour.

Case example: Robert is a tall, strapping 15-year old. Upon receiving Robert's report card, his father was quite mystified as to why the physical education mark was a failing grade: "The math I can understand, but how can you possibly flunk gym?" Robert's father spoke with the physical education teacher who described a typical situation in class: "Robert is all enthusiastic when he starts the circuit training, but not even half-way through he either sits down or leaves whining, 'I don't want to - it's too hard.' If Robert will not cooperate, I have no choice but to fail him." In this instance, Robert's medical evaluation later confirmed that he in fact has decreased muscle bulk and power and has very low tone in his muscles (hypotonicity, or "flabby" muscles) causing him to become quickly fatigued with prolonged movement or activity. Further, it was discovered that he was also having problems in Construction class, where he would refuse to use any type of power tool. Review of his medical assessment revealed that he has motor problems with reflexes, hand-eye coordination and visual-spatial difficulties. As a result, he would intentionally shy away from using these tools, because he knew he was not going to be able to control them very well. This was compounded by his difficulties in communication skills: he was unable to verbalize his concerns. Robert also has tremendous problems, due to his central nervous system disruption, with settling into sleep and in getting up in the morning. The transition or "feeling" to get up from the sleep-to-wake cycle is not physiologically available to him, so he is notoriously late for morning classes, and this tardiness is reflected in his academic success.

Case example: 20-year-old Derek is placed in a supported independent living residence, and is noted by staff to be a constant complainer: "my legs hurt . . . my arms hurt . . . my knees hurt . . . my elbow hurts . . . my back hurts . . . my toe hurts." Unknowingly, assumptions are made that he is likely seeking attention, is lazy and is perceived as oppositional when he does not complete chores that involve more strenuous physical activity. File records indicate that Derek has had "growing pains" since his early childhood. Based on his medical diagnosis of FASD, a diligent staff member considers the possibility that Derek may have some problems with his bone structure, and makes an appointment to see a specialist. A skeletal x-ray reveals that Derek has several parts of his body including his neck, back and knees that are not "fused" properly, causing him chronic discomfort. This is not to suggest that he had sub-optimal care by his previous group home staff and/or foster parents. In their defence, Derek was not diagnosed with FASD until he was nearly 18 years of age. He also had a history of behavioural problems that were linked to physical abuse and neglect that he experienced prior to his placement in foster care; thus, the physical ramifications of his disability were not considered.

Planning for future employment should consider not only the individual's strengths in cognition and overall abilities, but also a complete overview of his or her physical make-up so that there is no risk for further complications to body structure and overall health. As a society we tend to group kids who have not been able to complete high school by steering them into manual labour employment, thinking that this would be in their best interest. This was also the case for Robert until it was discovered that he has mild thoracic scoliosis and a vertebrae not formed the way it should be. Heavy lifting not only would likely aggravate his condition but could cause permanent damage. For patients like Robert (now 18), the **OBD** 3 Step Plan of Action! focuses on his strengths: long-term memory, love of animals, and if he is shown by actual demonstration, ability to catch on quite quickly. After being included in the process of discovery and "out-of-the-box thinking," Robert has become today one of the finest dog groomers around!

Another physical issue common to patients of this diagnosis is mid-facial hypoplasia, or a face that is too flat in the middle. In some cases, this can lead to multiple ear infections that could result in the placement of tubes in the ear(s). Some patients might develop scar tissue in the ear canal, leading to hearing loss which, if not noticed, could translate to the appearance of defiant behaviour.

Case example: Michelle is ten years of age and new to her current foster home. In the first few weeks, she is cooperative and helpful. Then her foster parents notice that she seems to be not following through with requests, and when asked to describe her behaviour they say she appears to have become a "selective listener." A case conference is held, and it is presumed that the "honeymoon period" is coming to an end and other possible behaviours are anticipated. Several days after this meeting, the foster mother notices that there is mucus on Michelle's pillow and discovers that she has developed a serious ear infection. Immediately Michelle is taken to the doctor where her ears are drained and treated. In this case, Michelle never complained because she has a high tolerance for pain, and impairment of her verbal processing skills (or ability to describe her feelings) makes it more difficult for her to communicate. What actually happened was that while the infection was developing, mucus was building and traveling up and down her ear canal, causing her hearing to fluctuate in and out like a "selective listener's." Now, with the development of a cold, Michelle's family makes an immediate doctor's appointment (she now has a specialist), and uses more visual cues, such as asking and pointing to her ears, to make it easier for her to understand and communicate.

The Central Nervous System controls a lot of things such as intelligence and brain functioning, attention span, balance, coordination, and the senses such as sensitivity to light, sound, touch and variations in appetite. Eating problems can occur in two ways. Some patients will not know when to stop eating and will eat until they literally throw up. Others will be completely disinterested in food and will refuse to eat or only eat very small portions at a time. The common denominator here is that their Central Nervous System has been permanently disrupted because part of the brain that controls these senses has been injured in fetal development. As a result they do not feel full or, conversely, feel hungry. Lack of appetite can also be compounded by medications and should be discussed with the child's physician to ensure the best possible plan. This may include carefully regulating food intake, or planning several small meals and supplementary drinks consistently throughout the day.

Case example: Candace is 14 years of age and very thin. Her teacher sees her throwing her homemade lunch in the garbage and questions her about it. Candace responds with "I'm not hungry." Alarmed at her response, the teacher questions her further and begins to counsel her with regard to the possibility of anorexia, a serious eating disorder that in the extreme can result in individuals starving themselves to death. Due to her problems with expressive and receptive language skills, Candace answers her teacher based on what she thinks it is the teacher wants her to say. By now, the concerned teacher is convinced that Candice requires immediate intervention. The teacher calls the parents in for an emergency meeting; however, in the mean time, Candace goes home crying, telling her parents that she thinks she did something wrong and that she is in trouble at school. She is also dreadfully upset that she is going to die in the near future, as that is basically what she "heard" or understood in the conversation with her teacher (she has trouble decoding long sentences). Her parents were beside themselves. They had never considered the possibility of anorexia, because a lack of appetite was always an issue for Candace from the time she was adopted at five years of age. Fortunately, Candace was scheduled for her FASD medical evaluation the same month, and a diagnosis was made which included the explanation of her eating habits and low weight to height being a direct result of her medical disposition (FASD). The school staff kindly agreed to be part of a new plan of having Candace "snack" throughout the day and monitoring her progress.

As children grow older, there may be other issues such as upper respiratory tract infections, viral infections, asthma emergencies, surgeries, not to mention the repeated visits to the Emergency Room for accidents involving bikes, bunk-beds, running, swinging, climbing, skate boarding, diving or standing. Janice, mother of seven-year-old Billy, shared that her son's chart at the local hospital is as large as the New York telephone book. She swears that some of the nurses and doctors still give her dirty looks as if she in some way is responsible for her son's death-defying performances, including eating a zipper (don't ask). Unfortunately, it is often the parent's appropriate actions or assumed inactions that have the potential to be misconstrued by others, again all because of a very complicated *physical* disability.

Many patients have more than one disability, such as vision problems and brain dysfunction. For children who are blind or hearing impaired, our homes and classrooms are modified to meet their needs, and this issue is no different. There are a variety of physical anomalies that can be associated with FASD. It is imperative that children at risk are medically evaluated thoroughly in order to make certain the appropriate treatment is available and to *prevent* any possibility of misunderstandings. This also applies to out-of-country adoptions because, regrettably, alcoholism is prevalent in all countries around the world, not just in North America. We are sometimes surprised by the incidence of FASD in other countries, like parts of Africa, for example, where some women are paid in wine instead of money for their labour at the wine manufacturing plants. No country is immune to the social influences linked to prenatal alcohol exposure. An accurate medical evaluation and explanation of these issues to others living with, related to, or working with our children is the first step in ensuring that misconceptions about patients and their families are kept at a minimum. Most importantly, precise medical assessment provides affected persons of all ages with the appropriate health care and essential treatments.

Chapter Three

Identifying Central Nervous System (CNS) dysfunction in your child

The first step in this exercise is to list all of the abilities, strengths and positive characteristics about your child that you can. Think of things that you like about your child, certain skills or attributes that you admire in his or her personality. These can be anything from a good sense of humour to being spontaneous or determined, to excelling in creative writing or athletics. We will refer to this throughout the book as the **Strengths List**!

Example:

<u>Trevor's Strengths, Abilities and Positive Characteristics</u>

Creative intelligence, musical, artistic

Great ability to build things with his hands

Has a fantastic recall of songs and loves to sing

Persistent, committed, determined

Friendly, trusting, sociable

Energetic, athletic, spontaneous

Affectionate, caring, compassionate

Sensitive, concerned, helpful

Is a wonderful storyteller

Loves animals and is good with small children

He is small in stature and uses it to his advantage

Make Your Child's **Strengths List!** here:

Strengths, Abilities and Positive Characteristics

Although there are many physical and cognitive similarities for FASD patients, remember that no two are ever affected the same way. This makes the detective work of identifying your child's specific issues more intricate but fascinating. Some will have a high tolerance for pain, some a low tolerance for pain and some may have a regular pain threshold, but all will have a diagnosis of FASD. These variables are present for physical anomalies, cognitive or "thinking" abilities and all other issues related to central nervous system dysfunction. This is why it is not helpful to overgeneralize about affected individuals. Now complete the next step by filling out the **Central Nervous System Checklist** by identifying the exact issues that pertain to your child, youth or adult. As dysfunction or damage to the Central Nervous System (CNS) is responsible for the interruptions in processing information, the results will vary; for example, some patients may be distractible but not have a hyperactivity component.

Central Nervous System Checklist

Check off the box if your child displays the identified behaviour (examples are for clarification only):

Impulsivity

❑ Do they do things impulsively without thinking things through?

❑ Does their tendency to be impulsive compromise their safety? (For example, they make a left turn on a bicycle without looking or signalling.)

Attention

❑ Do they have a diagnosis of Attention Deficit Disorder?

- ❑ Do they have difficulty making a transition from one activity to another, particularly if it is something that interests them?

- ❑ Do they have difficulty sustaining focus on a task, which has an impact on the quality of their learning experience? (Is the teacher saying there are attention/focus problems?)

Distractibility

- ❑ Do they have trouble keeping their attention on something (other than T.V. or computer games)?

- ❑ Are they easily sidetracked from their tasks? (For example, they become enthralled with an ant scurrying across the kitchen floor instead of completing their homework.)

Hyperactivity

- ❑ Do they have a diagnosis of Attention Deficit Hyperactivity Disorder?

- ❑ Do they often appear restless, fidget, wiggle or are constantly moving? Do they tap pencils, cutlery, chopsticks, channel changers on the table? Do they zoom, whiz, rocket, resemble a whirling dervish, tornado, or are literally able to run up a wall?

- ❑ Do they have difficulty engaging in an activity, which requires concentration and staying in one place? (Like church. Ok, bad example.)

Memory

- ❑ Have they been diagnosed with short-term or long-term memory deficit?

- ❏ Is their memory sporadic? (Short and/or long term memory seems faulty or appears to be misfiring).

- ❏ If an activity is interrupted, are they unable to recall where they left off?

- ❏ Are they better able to recall details of events according to their personal interest or emotional importance, rather than in chronological order? ("It was close to my birthday.")

- ❏ Do they require visual reminders? For example, to be in the same location, or with the same person in order to jar their memory?

- ❏ Do they have trouble remembering some parts of directions?

- ❏ Do they have an exceptional memory for things that happened a long time ago or for songs?

- ❏ Are they concrete thinkers and take things literally? (If you asked them to pick up their room would they tell you that it is too heavy?)

- ❏ Do they have trouble realizing that things are similar to each other?

- ❏ Do they have difficulty problem solving? (Did they initiate an unplanned bathroom renovation because you gave the instruction, "turn on the bath water" and forgot to specify "and then turn it off"?)

Abstract Concepts

- ❏ Do they have trouble recognizing that there is more than one way to symbolize numbers and letters, for example, a = A or one = 1?

- Do they have a poor concept of time? (This may be indicated by showing up three days late for dinner.)

- Do they have trouble managing money or appreciating the value of items? (They think you're a scrooge because you won't buy them a 102-inch television set or install an indoor Olympic sized pool.)

- Do they struggle to learn multiplication tables (looks like smoke is coming from their ears when doing math homework)?

- Do they have trouble answering abstract questions or responding to a statement such as, "why?", "wait", "there will be consequences".

Sequencing

- Is it difficult for them to make a decision when presented with open-ended choices? ("What do you want to wear?" may result in a five-hour clothing try on spree or suspension for showing up at school naked.)

- The concept of "priority" does not mean anything to them at all? (Also applicable to husbands.)

- Is it difficult for them to organize themselves for activities or chores? (Have you caught them staring for long periods of time directly into the washing machine?)

- Do they get confused about where to start?

- Do they have trouble doing things in logical order?

- Is it difficult for them to see patterns?

❏ They are unable to follow through without assistance.

❏ Are they the type of kid who doesn't play imagination games like house, trucks, dolls or cashier?

Problem Solving

❏ Are they disorganized in their approach and find it hard to come up with solutions?

❏ Do they repeat the same mistakes until they become frustrated or simply quit trying?

❏ Do they repeat the same mistakes or behaviours even though they have received numerous consequences? (Again, applicable to husbands.)

❏ Does your child rely on signals to gain your attention such as waving, pointing, tapping, poking, staring, hollering, turning blue or grabbing?

❏ If you take something away that they are using or playing with, do they have a tendency to react in such a way that the neighbours are likely to call 911?

Communication skills

❏ Do they seem to have trouble expressing appropriate feelings that are usually attached to an action such as remorse? (They are saying they're sorry but you know that they're really not.)

❏ Do they have trouble remembering the words for things?

❑ Do they seem to have difficulty following instructions? (They might either complete the first, middle or last part of the instructions or do them in reverse.)

❑ Are they able to memorize information but not be able to explain it to you or apply it?

❑ Do they have difficulty reiterating or retelling an event that has occurred to them in the correct order?

❑ Is it difficult for them to follow the progression (sequence) of a conversation, and do they then make out of context comments? (The family dinner conversation is discussing their sister's school day and they'll start talking about earth worms.)

❑ Are they not able to differentiate idiomatic language or double meaning words? (You ask them to draw the drapes, and they spend an hour colouring a picture of them?)

❑ Do they perseverate on a particular thought, topic or experience, not being able to let something go. ("Can I have a motorcycle?, Can I have a motorcycle?, Can I have a motorcycle?", Day 9 - "Can I have a motorcycle?")

❑ Do they hear an experience from someone else and repeat it as their own?

❑ Do they have decoding problems where they may comprehend only every third word of a sentence? (Do they "fill in the blanks" in order to compensate, and this sometimes looks as if they are lying?)

❑ Do they repeat back a request verbatim, but do not follow through? (You: "What did I just ask you to do?" Child: "Tidy up your room" and then you watch them walk past the bedroom and start playing Nintendo.)

❑ 876,341 repetitions are required to ensure they can *consistently* do the task without reminders?

Soft neurological signs

❑ Do they have visual depth perception problems (bumping into things), poor hand-eye coordination? (Do they knock the pickles over every time they go to take out the chocolate milk from the refrigerator?)

❑ Do they have difficulty filtering out stimuli such as bright lights, loud sounds, being touched, or being in groups or line-ups?

❑ Does it seem to take them longer than other kids to grasp concepts?

❑ Do they tire easily?

❑ Do they have "tight or flabby" muscle tone?

❑ Do they seem to have either a very high tolerance for pain or very low tolerance for pain? (They crash into a tree and keep on going even though the bump on their forehead is swelling larger than a grapefruit, or they'll become hysterical with the slightest scratch.)

❑ Are they constantly making odd or unusual sounds or movements?

❑ Do they have sensitivities to combination foods

(several textures together) such as chili made with beef, beans, onions and tomatoes?

❑ Do they have disrupted sleep patterns? Are they difficult to settle into sleep, awake during the night and hard to get up in the morning?

❑ Is your child a "Daredevil"? (They will jump off the roof donned only with a towel-cape or they will go with a stranger, not realizing the potential danger in a situation?)

❑ Will they continue to eat until you stop them (my problem), or are they not particularly interested in food and are tough to feed?

Comprehension of social rules

❑ Is your child or teen a "collector of other people's things" and have trouble understanding the concept of ownership? (Unless it is theirs.)

❑ Do they have difficulty sharing? (Like a husband with the remote control.)

❑ Are they "social chameleons" where they imitate peer behaviours without discriminating between appropriate and inappropriate, and are very easily led?

❑ Do they stand too close (in other people's space), demonstrate inappropriate affection or misinterpret other's intentions?

Social emotional presentation

❑ Do they have difficulty understanding their own emotions and interpreting the emotions of others?

- ❏ Are they moody, which may cause them to overreact? (Does the phrase "Drama Queen" spring to mind?)

- ❏ Does your child have difficulty understanding how their behaviour impacts others? ("What do you mean you're mad at me just because I broke your great-great grandmother's heirloom one of a kind figurine?")

- ❏ Do they seem to have a low self-esteem no matter how hard you work at it?

- ❏ Do they blame others for problems (you, siblings, pets, teachers, the media)?

- ❏ Are they immature for their age in emotional functioning where their behaviour is often demonstrated as that of a much younger child? ("You shut up, no you shut up, that's not FAIR!" (not to be confused with an argument with your spouse - ok, my spouse.)

Now that you have completed the **Central Nervous System Checklist**, you have the second tool we will use to construct and determine strategies in order to reduce the incidence of negative behaviours. We will be referring to it as the **CNS List**. (It might be enlightening to fill one out on your spouse but be prepared; my husband qualifies for 92% of the behaviours on the list.) Once we appreciate that these types of CNS dysfunction intricacies *translate* to the appearance of seemingly wilful or defiant behaviours, we are better able to design prevention strategies and intervention techniques, based on the individual's respective **strengths** and **abilities**.

Chapter Four

Can YOU relate?

In this chapter we are going to take a realistic look at how **all of us** (yes, even you) have behaviours that drive other people crazy. The intention here is for us to realise that we all possess some of these traits. Affected individuals merely have more of them, more often. We will also examine how it *feels* when some of these "brain idiosyncrasies" happen to us. By doing so, we can relate to how tough it is for our kids who are so often misunderstood and reprimanded for things they have no control over. In truly understanding their plight, we may find it much easier to have patience and a positive approach.

Impulsivity, attention, distractibility and hyperactivity

As an ADD adult I can speak with some authority in explaining how it feels to be extremely impulsive. Impetuous, rash, reckless, irresponsible, hasty, spontaneous, brash, impatient, have a lack of focus and hurried - all the time. That's the short list from my grade two report card. Trying to diet is murder as I can tell myself over and over, "I'm not going to eat that chocolate cake - I'm not going to eat that chocolate cake," and before I know it, there are only crumbs left on the plate. Then I wonder, "When did that happen?" as if I wasn't physically present for the whole event. I tend to have a few more bruises than other people as I walk into things more frequently, regularly eat cold toast that I've forgotten about and have nearly burned down the house at least once a week in repeated attempts to make rice on the stove because I have to boil it for a while and then turn it down. I'm usually distracted after four seconds at the pre-boil stage.

All of us have various abilities in maintaining attention and focus. As adults, we all move at different speeds from a snail's pace to roadrunner. The hyperactive component for adults is the type A personality who rarely sits, talks fast, walks fast and has peculiar sleeping habits. They are the ones who usually don't need a diet. ADHD adults describe their feelings: "Sometimes, especially when I'm tired, I'm so anxious and wired inside that I feel like I am physically going to be lifted off the ground." That's why people with some types of CNS dysfunction find themselves using heavy comforters and gravitate (literally) towards backpacks instead of briefcases - the weight makes them feel more secure and "grounded," as opposed to that "spinning off your nut" feeling that we get that is most difficult to control.

How impulsivity, attention, distractibility and hyperactivity *translates* to behaviours

As described earlier, most alcohol-affected patients come with a secondary diagnosis of Attention Deficit Disorder (ADD) or Attention Deficit Hyperactivity Disorder (ADHD). As a direct result of wandering attention and distractibility, they lose stuff - a lot. Parents are quick to tell us that they have replaced twelve pair of mittens, three coats (left on the playground), four pairs of glasses (sat on, stepped on or scratched beyond recognition), eight bus passes, retainers, shoes, and the plate sent to school with the Halloween cookies. Is it intentional? No. Is it frustrating? Absolutely. Learn to anticipate that when children are created with the ability to be totally distracted from a task when a fly buzzes by, that they are going to lose stuff. Count on it and anticipate replacement costs.

Another example of potentially misinterpreted behaviour is that of a teenager who has received 42 tickets for not paying for the Light Rail Transit. He is then Court Ordered to pay restitution of his fines by volunteering at a soup kitchen across town. His group home staff person has ridden with him several times on the bus to prepare him for going on his own. He successfully travels twice to his destination, but on the third try he doesn't show up and calls the staff five hours later asking them to pick him up on the furthest end of the city. He then has to return to Court, is sternly lectured and receives yet more hours of community service. Did he do this on purpose because he just didn't want to pay the transit fare? Is he defiant of authority figures? In his case, he got on the transit intending to go to the soup kitchen. He sits by the window to watch for landmarks so he knows where to get off. But then, an older lady sits next to him and strikes up a conversation. She is nice to him and is interested in what he has to say. When it comes to her stop, he looks up and realizes that nothing is familiar. So he stays on the train, hoping to recognize something, and eventually gets off on the other side of town. Confused, he walks aimlessly around finding even more distractions from his dilemma (like a pet store) until he finds a phone and calls for help. The irony here is in the initial charges that led up to this situation, where he was caught without a ticket numerous times in the first place. Why? Unlike the bus system where he has a visual cue (the bus driver) to remind him to pay when he gets on the bus, the Light Rail Transit system does not provide a human cashier. He is supposed to know and remember to purchase a ticket at the dispenser first and then take it on the train with him. There is no one there to remind him to pay. It is situations like this that continue to perpetuate the misinterpretation of the youth's behaviour, and in some instances are responsible for prolonging his involvement within the Justice system. On the upside, he is really enjoying his new fish that he admired at the pet shop.

Memory, abstraction and sequencing

Do you ever notice that your husband seems to have great difficulty remembering to pick up one grocery item, but can recall the name, age, number, chronological history of touchdowns, penalties, yards run and injuries of the players in the entire football league? In fairness, let me ask you if the following scenario has ever happened to you. You are working on a project out in the garage and you need a certain tool. You walk from the garage through the yard, into the laundry room, past the den into the kitchen and then it happens . . . you ask yourself, "What in blazes did I come in here for?" You are laughing because you have experienced this and, if you're over 40, likely with more frequency than you would care to admit. A blonde moment, senior's moment, peri-MENTAL-pause - call it what you will, it happens to all of us. However, can you predict how many times a day or week this experience will occur? No - because memory is *sporadic*. The next time this happens to you, think about the emotions you go through in 30 seconds. First you feel perplexed (what did I come in here for?), then you graduate to frustrated (*what did I come in here for?*), and then you become agitated, as you know it's in your head but you cannot pull it out. The next emotion you may experience is panic - WHY CAN'T I REMEMBER WHAT I CAME IN HERE FOR? Now let's take this one further. You're still standing in the kitchen, by now examining your cuticles as you have forgotten why you are there, and your spouse stomps into the house, visibly angry: " If you didn't want to do this project you should have just said so!" Now you are receiving a consequence for something you simply don't remember. For some alcohol-affected individuals, this type of erratic memory loss can occur up to 90 percent of their day and they could be unintentionally disciplined because of it.

How memory, abstraction and sequencing *translates* to behaviours

Kids are inadvertently punished for their memory deficits in many ways throughout their day. At school, the teacher may spend extra time with your child all afternoon going through a new concept step by step and repeat it until satisfied that the child "gets it." The next morning, the child returns to class and teacher does a review of the same material, but the student looks up and says, "I don't remember." The frustrated teacher states firmly, albeit unwittingly to the seemingly defiant student, "You are being lazy now. Go to the office until you produce this work." Friends could also reprimand. 15-year-old Jessica comes home from school hysterically crying because her best friend accused her of stealing and refuses to have anything to do with her. Weeks earlier she had asked her friend if she could borrow a music CD, and they agreed that she would return it at the end of the week. She forgot. The friend reminded her at the end of the day and she repeated to herself "CD, CD, CD" all the way home on the bus, but when she got home there was company, so she visited and completely forgot again. The following week her girlfriend reminded her on the phone, so she took the CD to the front door and put it on her shoes (a memory trick her mother taught her) so she would remember to take it the next day. Morning came and it had snowed, so she went to the back door where her boots are kept, and, yes, forgot the CD. Having memory deficits is extremely frustrating for the patients to deal with when they have to think so hard to remember and are also then forced to deal with other people's displeasure and possibly disciplinary actions as well.

The easiest way to define abstract concepts is: things you cannot see. If you can't see it, feel it, touch it - it is an abstract concept. If you can see it, it is a concrete concept.

Predicting the future requires the ability to **compare** (put things side by side to evaluate them), **contrast** (distinguish the differences between things), **associate** (link the information), **abstract** (understand a concept without being able to physically see it), **sequence** (put a chain of events or things in the right or logical order) and **generalize** (reduce the information and make it straightforward). The concept of time being abstract is confusing. We can see time with a clock, but if we do not have access to a timepiece (for example, when camping or on a watch-free holiday), how do we know what time it is? Ever play the "How close is it to supper time" game where you all try to guess the time? You do so by using a combination of skills: First, your memory allows you to associate what you've learned from the past; for example, last week when the sun was dimmer, it was five o'clock. Your ability to compare and contrast brings that information forward and allows you to apply it to a similar situation (today). The intact brain allows you to associate, mentally visualize an abstract concept (time), sequence (put the information in logical order) and generalize the information in order to tell the time. We also use internal feelings to help us tell time. Have you ever experienced a morning where you are mentally awake before you open your eyes and you think to yourself, "I'm late!"? You roll over to check the time and sure enough, you're late. How do you know that? It's a *feeling* you have when your CNS is working for you.

Many patients with CNS disruption simply don't get that feeling and have to rely on supports to assist them. We cannot heal FASD brains and make them *feel* things that they are not physiologically capable of. Fortunately, though, we are able to creatively teach to their particular learning style and recognize that we may need to make some adjustments for them in order to find their best fit. By law, we build bigger doorframes and ramps for persons that require a wheelchair, and we are happy to do so. Certain modifications for persons with this disability should be no different.

Cause-and-effect thinking is basically "if I do this, this will happen." Countless children are not able to formulate this concept because it is a form of abstract thinking. For example, children may be playing with a toy and not realize the force that they are using (cause), and secondly, they do not recall what happened the last time they damaged the same toy (effect). The combination of these issues can lead to the common "cat-contortion" incidents, where some kids may be unusually rough with animals, such as twisting them into pretzel-like figures. In many cases, they do not realize they may be squeezing too hard and they do not put together that "if I rearrange the cat, I will hurt it" or that it will hurt them. In addition, for children that have a high tolerance for pain, a massacre of cat scratches does not act as a deterrent because they may not feel the same pain as another child might. Or, individuals with severe memory deficits may have completely forgotten the pain they experienced the last time they were scratched, and they repeat the same experience (kind of like the pain we seem to forget all about when we decide to have another baby). For some children the cat is no different than the stuffed toy cat that they sleep with every night.

Sequencing is putting things in logical order. Unfortunately, in this category all my examples are again husband-related. For every day of our married life I have asked my husband the same question: "What would you like for dinner?" and every day he stares at me like a deer in the headlights. (Of course you're wondering which one of us is not learning from repeated consequences because I'm daft enough to keep asking him and secretly hoping that some day he'll actually have an answer.) Nonetheless, if I say, "Would you like chicken or steak for dinner?" his response is immediate. Don't even get me started on setting priorities around the house and as far as sequencing chores like doing dishes, which usually entails glasses first, then china and greasy pans last (unless you're married to you-know-who that swears by the "biggest to smallest" dishwashing theory). Then there's laundry: Separate colours, whites first, change temperatures, adjust to Permanent Press or Delicate, add soap prior to rinse cycle, fabric softener in the dispenser and not in combination with soap - well, you get the picture. As you can see, both tasks have many steps that require a particular sequence, as do endless other day-to-day skills. For children, youth and adults that do not have the "connectors" to put things together in the correct order, a part of every day is dependant on help from others to get it right.

Problem solving

"My child does not learn from consequences" has to be the number one hit on the "What drives me to homicidal tendencies" behaviours list. Nonetheless, consider this scenario: At a party recently, my girlfriends and I have surrounded the snack table, talking and, of course, eating. Then all of a sudden, my husband hollers across the room, "Hey, Liz, didn't you say that you're up to 163 pounds?" As the room fills with looks of horror from all the women and sympathetic groans from the men, my friend Emilia pipes up in an attempt to ease the tension by asking, "So, who brought the dip?" Never one to miss an opportunity I respond, "I did - he's standing over there with Jim." Now I ask you - were there clues (or cues) to help him understand that he should never do this again? Sure. Fiery glares (a visual cue), silence and later screaming in the car (auditory cues), the slug in the arm when he gets home (tactile cue), followed by a clear, concise, verbal instruction: "if you ever do that again, you will have two choices - divorce or death." After all of this, does he do it again? Yup, because he thinks he didn't do anything wrong! According to him, he told the truth (ouch) and is completely puzzled at my reaction, because I was the one that discussed the information in the first place. He also has the worst memory for things if it doesn't mean much to him (something we have in common). On the plus side, he apparently doesn't see me being tubby as a problem. In cases where children, youth and adults are consistently repeating the same mistakes due to a combination of processing deficits, they simply do not understand what they did wrong. That is why they are much more likely to do it again.

How problem solving *translates* to behaviours

Being able to solve problems requires a number of abilities. To do so, we must take stored information from a past experience and transfer it to the current situation. To apply that information, it takes planning (what do I do next?) which entails putting the information in logical order (sequencing abilities). The major component in solving a problem is the ability to interpret an abstract concept or things we cannot see. A common behaviour attached to immature problem solving skills occurs when you take away something that belongs to children, and it leads to an outburst more appropriate for cancelling Christmas. The main difficulty here is that what they *see* is the item leaving them, and what they are unable to formulate is that it will eventually come back to them. The item *returning* to them is an abstract concept. In situations like this you are asking them to imagine and anticipate it coming back to them, which they are not able to do. For affected youth and adults the concept of someone taking their things away is interpreted as permanently gone, never to return. Naturally, if someone took our possessions forever, we too might have a volatile reaction. The same holds true for the bathtub example when the water is running over the tub and they leave the bathroom to go watch a movie. The identical skills are necessary in order to solve that problem, and when those abilities are not available to them, it appears that they are willingly trying to upset you. This is why in many instances they rely so much on you to be their "external brain" to help them in solving daily predicaments.

Communication skills

Do they have trouble remembering the words for things? Hah! When you were growing up, did your mother ever call out, "Where's the ah, the ah, oh, you know the uh, whachamacallit," to the point where all you wanted to do was squeeze the word out of her? I've discovered that I owe her a formal apology for becoming perturbed with her, because I'm now regularly forgetting the word that is used to identify myself - like my name. We all have some trouble with word retrieval at various times, but some persons with disabilities experience it with more frequency. Consider the earlier example of the "I brought the dip" story. After the explosion that ensues when you leave the party, your spouse makes a decision based on what he sees. The histrionics and voice inflection tell him that he should apologize, so he says, "Well, I'm sorrrrrry." Nice. Is he really sorry? Not exactly. Does he seem to have a lack of remorse? You bet. Why? Again, because he thinks he didn't do anything wrong. For individuals that truly don't understand what they did wrong, they will say they're sorry because you tell them to by your words (telling them to say sorry), voice tone (sounds like they are in trouble), and body language (your face literally has a knot in it so they get the picture that you are displeased with them). This doesn't mean they are socio-pathological; rather, they do not have the more intact higher order thinking mechanisms to read between the lines and organize information as we do. Affected individuals can sound "flat" or uncaring, and we could assume they don't have the emotional capacity to feel, which is often not true. It is actually the difficulty they have adequately expressing themselves that is misinterpreted, because it does not coincide appropriately to the emotional situation.

How communication skills *translate* to behaviours

Dandy examples: Joey is ten years old and is refusing to attend another appointment with his new therapist. There is concern that she may have touched on a sensitive issue or that he is in denial or avoidance, or has been abused in some way. When I went out to visit him, I asked him how he liked his new therapist? He responded, "She is sooo stupid!" "Why do you think she is stupid, Joey?" "Do you know what she asked me? She asked me if I was BLUE," he said, as he checked his skin to make sure it was still the right colour. Affected kids can be very literal. Take 15-year-old Sam whose principal's severe tongue-lashing ended with "And when you *hit the door* of your classroom, you will behave!" You guessed it - he walloped it so hard that it nearly came off the hinges, and then he quietly sat down. This scene really smacked of being a "trouble-maker," when in fact he essentially did what he was told.

Another glitch in communication for some patients is called "borrowing utterances." They repeat something they have heard someone else say and apply it to themselves as fact. A young boy demonstrated an excellent example of this while on a weekend visit with his father. The same week he had started attending a new school, and Monday morning his teacher inquired as to how he enjoyed his weekend. "Well, there was a stabbing in the apartment and a big fire!" he alleged. Naturally, the shocked teacher and principal contacted the mother with their concerns. Thankfully, the parents were on good terms and jointly probed further into his story. Initially perplexed, the father eventually figured out that they had watched the evening news while they were eating dinner and a stabbing in an apartment and a fire in another apartment were the lead reports. The boy had reiterated the information as his own, not maliciously, but because of the complexities of his ability to process and interpret information. Plus, a very captive audience (the unknowing teacher and principal) unintentionally rewarded him by their facial expressions and immediate worry, which reinforced his statements and cued him to continue.

A more serious incident of communication problems concerned a little girl who was interviewed by a Social Worker and a Police Officer because there was a report to Child Welfare authorities that she may have been sexually abused. During the interview she continued to play and answer the questions directly and with graphic detail. Her voice never quaked, she didn't cry, and her overall presentation seemed to be a "matter-of-fact" attitude. The Officer had doubts that anything had occurred because her emotional and verbal presentation was dissimilar to what one would expect from a child who had been so drastically assaulted. Nonetheless, shortly after the interview the mother called in saying she had found physical evidence of sexual assault, which confirmed the child's disclosure. She did not have the same intrinsic communication skills that other children possess, so it *appeared* that this little girl wasn't traumatized by the abuse. In fact, she clearly was distressed, as indicated by her demonstration of non-verbal, volatile behaviours (bedwetting and physical aggression towards her peers). It is imperative that we closely examine the communication abilities of our affected children, youth and adults as they have ramifications for home life, academics, and relationships, and in some cases legal issues.

Soft neurological signs

Soft neurological signs are definitely things that we can all relate to. Let's start with **visual depth perception**. I have a girlfriend whose depth perception is so distorted that her family draws straws to see who has to get into the car with her behind the wheel. The last time I sat in the passenger's seat, she nearly grazed her own house while backing out of the driveway. I noticed there were already scrapes on the siding and on the large decorative rock that is placed in the middle of her lawn. On the freeway other drivers sped by, waving numerous hand gestures because, as she puts it, "I have a little trouble staying in my aisle." Coming to a full stop behind another car puts new meaning to the distance of the millimetre. However, on the upside, the experience does manage to make one's hair fuller. On returning from our trip, the garage door opened and revealed a tennis ball dangling from the ceiling. When I inquired as to its purpose she explained, "Oh, Paul put that up so when it touches the windshield I know when to stop" (as we crashed into a stack of boxes). Visual depth perception is best described as an off-kilter sense of seeing - things may be closer or farther than they appear. Ever notice that the side view mirror of a car has a disclaimer reading, "Things may be closer than they appear," just as you back into a pole at the Wal-Mart? Depth perception can definitely lead to the appearance of negative behaviour, as demonstrated in the hall of a school where another student slightly brushes by a child who then screams, "He hit me!" There is a possibility that such children's sense of "close" is exaggerated, or they could be extremely sensitive to touch resulting in their brain misreading that the other child actually hit them. One dad's observation of his son illustrates: "When he is looking down he'll hit his head on a tree, but if he is looking up, he'll trip over the roots - it's the way he sees the world."

As discussed earlier, **eating inconsistencies** are often caused by Central Nervous System dysfunction. I'm convinced that's my problem. Some patients may never feel full or, conversely, not feel hungry. Certain medications may also affect appetite and should be discussed with a doctor. Dealing with eating irregularities are most frustrating for us particularly because we are taught in our society that one of the components of good parenting is to feed our children well. If you come from an ethnic background like mine where eating is associated with giving, guilt, loving, mourning, celebration, depression, excitement, boredom, decadence and frugalness, you're pretty much ticked when someone doesn't want to eat your food. It insults you and sometimes embarrasses you, especially when no matter how much food your child eats, he or she could still be a poster-child for malnutrition in a third world country. The bottom line is: If the only sandwich texture children can tolerate and enjoy is cheese and raspberry jam, give them cheese and jam seven days a week, three hundred and sixty-five days a year. No child is in jeopardy from a surplus of crushed fruit. Be aware that it might be *our need* for variety as well as societal pressures that interferes with such decisions.

Over-sensitivities to stimuli like light, touch, sound or crowds are a result of the "filter" being on the blink. We all have filters to help us screen out stimuli, and to some extent these are variable. For example, on a warm sunny day you have the radio blaring with songs from your youth and you're singing and bobbing your head like a hyperactive turtle. You get home and jump out of the car. The next morning you get back into the car, turn the key and are nearly blown through the roof, while you frantically try to find the off button before your eardrums explode. Why? Because your filter is gauged by **your** control and it's working the way it's supposed to. Yesterday, the sound you preferred was much louder than today. This type of CNS disruption means that you cannot control it - it is **not** working for you, so lights are brighter, sounds may seem much louder and crowds make you feel like bees are swarming you. You'll notice that all of us have reactions to such annoyances. We may become agitated or short tempered, or abruptly leave a room, so the "overreactions" of affected persons in such situations are certainly understandable.

Let's talk about **fear** and the lack of it. Have you ever had the experience late at night where you are walking to your car by yourself and hear heavy footsteps behind you? Ever notice the physical changes that gradually transform your body? First, you may start walking a bit faster and your heart rate excels. The hair on the back of your neck might stand up, and mentally, you start planning your defence of fashioning a weapon with your keys while rehearsing your Miss Piggy "Hi-yah!" karate kick. You feel tense as your body tightens up and your breathing nearly stops. Why does this happen? Fear is a feeling. Your operative central nervous system and processing abilities combined tell you that there is danger. Your brain recalls and assesses previous experience, transfers it to the here and now, and applies that information warning you about "stranger-danger." Any patient from two to a hundred and two years of age whose brain has been compromised in a combination of areas may not *feel* scared. When you or I stand too close to the edge at the top of a mountain, our brain and body tell us to step back for there is danger of falling. You may be the parent in the front row of the roller coaster (with or without the kids) or the one holding the coats, more than happy to be on secure ground, as we all have different comfort zones. Similarly, with all facets of brain injury, it is important to realize that having a lack of fear puts persons with disabilities at lifelong risk for accidents and possible victimization. The good news is that there are lots of careers that pay very well for those that are not afraid of heights!

How soft neurological signs *translate* to behaviours

Over-sensitivity or **under-sensitivity** to cold or hot sensations can also translate to the appearance of uncooperative behaviour. Case example: In an FASD seminar for foster parents, there were numerous comments regarding the weather that day because it was extremely cold for the season. I asked the group how many of their foster children had run out of the house with no coat, no mittens, no hat, or a combination of all three. Over half of the room shot up their arms and one woman jumped up and gleefully announced, "but my kid remembered his back-pack today!" and the crowd wildly applauded. Coupled with Attention Deficit Hyperactivity Disorder, a "dulled" sense of feeling cold is often the source of this seemingly defiant behaviour.

Affected children and their families live with unpredictability from day to day due to inconsistencies in the patient's physiological make-up. Difficulty with transitions, such as from the sleep-to-awake cycle, getting ready for bed, or moving from one activity to another, can look as if they're being purposefully defiant, stubborn or just plain obstinate. No one needs a four-hour shower. Disrupted sleep patterns, or difficulty settling into sleep, awaking during the night and getting up in the morning, are usually not a choice but are caused by brain dysfunction. They are symptoms of the medical disposition of Fetal Alcohol Spectrum Disorder. In this case, it is again about feelings. As discussed earlier, some affected individuals do not have that inner clock to rely on to lull them to sleep, stay asleep and/or wake up. It is taxing to live with a small child that stays up in the night or is difficult to get up in the morning, but it seems to particularly bother us with our teenagers or adults even though this has been a consistent pattern, likely since birth. In general, teenagers physically require much more sleep, so when this need is combined with an initial sleep disorder, it's little wonder that we may have to forklift some kids to get them out of bed. The bottom line is that the bigger they are the more we expect from them, and sometimes we forget that we have no cure for FASD. They're likely going to be night owls forever. What we can do is adjust our way of thinking and provide reasonable options in time management that work with their special needs. Thankfully, in this day and age, we have 24-hour grocery stores and countless types of jobs readily available to those who are more attuned to their biological clock.

A common trait amongst affected persons is often either a **high sensitivity to pain** or, conversely, **a low or decreased sensitivity to pain**. The latter is most certainly an area to be recognized in a new living environment or at school. It may require extra attention since patients may be at higher risk for frostbite, burns or undetected injury. Case example: A ten-year-old girl returns from recess complaining that her arm is sore from hanging on the monkey bars. The teacher examines the arm and finds that she can rotate the arm with little complaint. During the afternoon the teacher continues to monitor her movements, which seem to be of no concern. Two days later, the child's mother contacts the school because her daughter's shoulder is discoloured and later found to be dislocated. In this case, the assumption of negative behaviour is not with the child, but associated with the teacher, as the mother was concerned that her child's injury was not reported to her. Further, when the mother took the child to the hospital she was questioned why the child did not receive medical attention sooner, because there were assumptions of physical neglect by the parents. In both instances these conjectures were certainly not the case.

Is your child or teen hard on things, breaking them, destructive? There may be a combination of neurological problems at hand, including having a high tolerance for pain, which in turn is an indicator of a "dulled" sense of feeling in the hands (and everywhere else). This makes it difficult for children to actually feel how hard they are manipulating an object. For example, if you slam your hand down on a table, it stings. If you put a glove on your hand and then slam it down on the table, it does not sting as much, if at all. Some affected individuals have the "gloved" hand because the damage to their central nervous system affects their sensory feelings, and they cannot determine or feel the amount of force. This is why if you choose to spank your child it is recommended that you use your bare hand, because you are not able to *feel* how hard you are actually spanking with an object and can cause injury. For children that do not have the ability to draw cause-and-effect conclusions such as "If I slam this toy down on the floor, it will break," the result is likely to be toy-bits, tears and rock and roll (literally).

The concept of value is frequently distorted for persons with disabilities; therefore, many affected children and youth seem to disregard possessions of their own and of others. Remember, value is an abstract concept - you can't see or touch value. One area to consider if you are caring for a child with this kind of amalgamation is to evaluate whether it is realistic to purchase costly toys or items that may be quickly destroyed. Be aware that this may provoke feelings of resentment such as "We buy him nice things and he doesn't appreciate them." Many parents have found a simple solution to these problems: they become garage sale and second hand store groupies! This way, they are able to purchase a number of items that may be only cents in monetary value but will prove invaluable in reducing immense stress for the entire family.

Heightened sense of smell can trigger negative reactions. Let's face it, certain aromas can incite an unenthusiastic response in all of us, which, if not aerated quickly, could lead to wild arm flapping, facial twisting, and/or extreme breath-holding contests. To an affected child smells may be more potent than to us because of an inoperable filter. How could smell translate to negative behaviour? Tommy begins grade three and comes home and tells his father that his teacher "stinks." We assume he clearly doesn't care for her educational prowess. Day's later he is sent home because he grabbed her necklace, ripped it off her neck and threw it across the room. Tommy had never displayed any such behaviour previously, so, needless to say, the parent-teacher-principal meeting was strained. After the meeting the father noted to his wife, "Did you notice that her perfume was quite heavy?" Upon further investigation and reconstruction of the events they solved the mystery. The teacher was wearing overpowering perfume and a dangling necklace. She leaned over to help him with a problem, and between his over-sensitivity to the smell and the over-stimulation of the necklace too close to his face flickering back and forth, Tommy reacted - with gusto. The teacher graciously agreed to tone down her perfume and jewellery. There has not been another incident to date.

A change in routine for some people can be disastrous. Do you know anybody who when the morning routine is changed takes on a Frankenstein or zombie-like appearance of communication? Did you know that if you are startled when you wake up (like pots crashing in the kitchen), you actually have an increased chance of dropping things throughout the day? This is because you have experienced some disruption to your central nervous system operations. Persons with various types of CNS dysfunction need routine like we all need air. It helps them know what to anticipate and what to do next. Regular routine helps them to do things the same way everyday as much as possible. The big bonus is that it minimizes stress for not only them but the entire family.

Comprehension of social rules

Jerry Seinfeld did an entire show on close talkers. You've met them - they stand so close to you that you could count their facial hair follicles. By now you're probably ahead of me for this one, but I'll lay it out anyway. What happens to you when someone is in your space? You lean backwards to distance yourself further to a more comfortable zone. How do you know that he or she is in your space? Because it's an internal feeling! Some people with this type of wiring don't get that *feeling* of personal boundary distance and can be misconstrued as being rude, intimidating or inconsiderate. This is exacerbated for kids dealing with personal relationships, as they will not understand why people react to them negatively. The basis of understanding another person's situation is to compare it and relate to it from our own experience. If this awareness is not available to them, it becomes confusing, especially when we expect them to "walk in our shoes," predict how another person might react, and then act accordingly.

How comprehension of social rules *translate* to behaviours

Ah, the **collectors of other people's things**. You may know them as Katie the Cat Burglar, Billy the Bandit, Robert the Robber, Polly the Pickpocket, Shamus the Shoplifter or Chris the Crook. Stealing is a big no-no in our society, and we generally don't like people who make off with our things. So why, no matter how hard we try, do some FASD-affected kids continue to pilfer anything and everything big or small, shiny or dull, useful or not useful? In discussing these behaviours with parents, I always ask whether their child *consistently* takes things of value (money, cars, credit cards) or takes virtually anything like a candy, paperclips and the inner workings of a toaster from the dump. If your answer is virtually anything, here's how it works:

Hazel is 12 years of age and is sitting across from her mother's friend, Ms. Bergen, who has her purse on her lap. Hazel is able to understand ownership at this time as the purse is in close proximity to Ms. Bergen (in her lap). Ms. Bergen decides to walk to the other room, leaving the purse on the table. Hazel looks at the purse, *does not see anyone attached to it*, and takes it to her room. When confronted, Hazel insists that she found the purse and that it is hers. For Hazel, even though Ms. Bergen was with the purse a few seconds ago and gave her the opportunity to *visually* recognize ownership, the purse is now by itself with no visual attachment (cue - Ms. Bergen) to help her process ownership. She is in the "here and now," and as far as she is concerned, she only took it from an empty space, not a person, because there was no person with the purse at the time.

There are intermingled processing problems that lead to this behaviour:

1) **Impulsivity:** "I see it - I want it - I take it!"

2) **Memory deficit:** Even though Ms. Bergen was there seconds ago, out of sight, out of mind is often the case with severe memory problems.

3) **Cause-and-effect thinking:** "If I do this, this will happen" is not a conversation in her head.

4) **Inability to process abstract thinking:** When she was in the room, Ms. Bergen was a concrete concept, but when she left the room, she then became an abstract concept.

Now I know what you're probably thinking if your child fits this profile: "Great, my kid's either going be the neighbourhood pariah or be in jail longer than Nelson Mandella." **NOT SO!** By first understanding where the behaviours are coming from, and teaching to your child's abilities, you can reduce the incidence of behaviours like stealing by using the OBD Three Step Plan of Action! So hang in there - help is on the way in Chapter 6!

Social emotional presentation

If your child has difficulty understanding his or her own emotions and interpreting the emotions of others, it is very possibly another indicator of CNS dysfunction. You'll notice that this phenomenon is also applicable to men and women, or as more recently described: "Venus vs. Mars." I mean really. A man having difficulty interpreting the emotions of his spouse - please! However, if you ask men the same question they may also suggest that women have certain emotional intricacies that are completely foreign to them. Apparently some men are very literal thinkers, which can lead to a marital glitch. I have a friend who told me that early on in her marriage she casually mentioned to her husband: "Flowers are so nice but then they die." She never saw another carnation for 23 years. All kidding aside, in order to act appropriately in social-emotional situations we have to have a basic understanding of communication skills, and be able to relate by sensing (feeling) the same things that the other person is feeling. There also has to be a proficiency to put it all together. By applying those abilities we are able to tend to someone else who is sad, empathize with someone who is frustrated, and be cautious when the other person is angry. Those without these advantages are often misunderstood as being uncaring, insensitive or hurtful, and it is the "missing links" in the brain that cause them to act in such a manner. They do care; they're just not able to show it or say it as we do.

How social-emotional presentation *translates* to behaviour

Jimmy is twelve years of age and is caught at recess inappropriately touching a six-year-old girl. The police and parents are contacted and a full investigation ensues. The boy is new into foster care and has a diagnosis of FASD; his cognitive abilities are considered average to low average. The social worker discovers that a psychologist had previously specified that, although he was in the average to low average range of intelligence, his developmental or age equivalent abilities in many areas (including social-emotional functioning) were estimated at between five and six years of age. My next question to you is this: What game have children through the ages conjured up at approximately age five? You guessed it - Doctor. "I'll show you my winkie if you show me your woo-hoo" kind of entertainment. A gentle reminder, this behaviour is apparently supposed to be continued later on as a regular adult activity. Nonetheless, when we discover our five-year-olds experimenting in this direction, we calmly as possible explain good touches and bad touches and perhaps beef up the supervision a bit. It is considered a natural course of action for most kids, but Jimmy at 12 could have been charged with a criminal offence, suspended from school, and sent to therapy to be assessed for the possibility of pedophiliac tendencies or past sexual abuse. To be clear, this particular child was not previously abused and did not have a psychiatric disorder. Although he is a big kid for 12 and at the lower end of average intelligence, *developmentally* he still functions in some areas as a five year old. This causes him to respond with the same maturity and level of comprehension of social rules as a child much younger than his chronological or actual age of 12. *This is not to suggest that this is the profile for **all** FASD children, youth or adults*. All patients require individual assessment to determine the processing possibilities and social history ramifications that may be resultant in certain behaviours. Precise treatment models are to be designed based on the totality of the information with the assistance of professionals trained in organic brain dysfunction.

In summary, all of us have different degrees of abilities and personal habits, FASD or no FASD. As human beings we have an incredible range of how the central nervous system works for us or how sometimes it doesn't. We all drive each other crazy in some way with our perceptions, actions, attitudes, and behaviour in relationships. Alcohol-affected folks just seem to do it more often because they were created differently. In appreciating that we are all not so different we are able to afford them more patience, understanding and kindness, and hopefully see some humour in ourselves and in our children's behaviour.

Chapter Five

Understanding your child's cognitive abilities

A cognitive or Psycho-Educational Assessment is required in conjunction with the medical evaluation in order to determine a diagnosis of Fetal Alcohol Spectrum Disorder. When you receive the results of the Psycho-Educational Assessment, arrange to speak with the Psychologist (Examiner) in order to have him or her explain what the results mean regarding your child's abilities. Everyone learns in different ways, and this is extremely important information to have in order to understand your child's specific learning style. This area is critical to the process of developing successful prevention and intervention strategies. This chapter contains the **Abilities List!** that you generate with the assistance of the psychologist that will be used in your **OBD** 3 Step Plan of Action!

Testing with regard to Fetal Alcohol Spectrum Disorders is broken down into several areas: Cognition, Communication, Academic achievement, Memory, Executive functioning and abstract reasoning, Attention Deficit/hyperactivity, and Adaptive behaviour, social skills and social communication. The names of the tests may vary because the Psychologist has several choices of appropriate tests to administer and assess within these domains.

To give you a head start in preparing for this meeting, here are some general terms to familiarize yourself with; followed by questions you may want to ask:

Terms:

Full Scale Intelligence Quotient (FSIQ) is a representation of a child's overall performance and is considered to be the best overall measure of general intelligence, cognitive ability, scholastic aptitude and readiness to master a school curriculum. FSIQ is the best indicator of I.Q. unless there is a significant scatter (peaks and valleys) in performance, and unless there is a significant (large) discrepancy between the Verbal I.Q. (VIQ) and Performance I.Q. (PIQ).

The **Verbal Scale I.Q. (VIQ)** assesses verbal comprehension and contains subtests that require a variety of oral verbal skills, verbal processing and memory. Or, *very basically,* in other words, it is the way a child processes or "hears" information that is said to them and how they are able to explain their thoughts. Verbal Scales: Input = Auditory channel and Output = Verbal channel.

The **Performance Scale I.Q. (PIQ)** measures non-verbal abilities, primary perceptual organization and abstract/visual reasoning, or, *very basically,* the actual doing of tasks.

*When there is an approximately 23 (or higher) point-difference between the Verbal I.Q. and the Performance I.Q. (in either direction), the Full Scale I.Q. is a poor estimate or is **not** an accurate representation of the individuals *overall* skills. It may also suggest a learning disability.

Learning Styles:

Each of us has an individual learning preference. Here are descriptions of some learning styles:

Auditory: Auditory learners take in information best

through verbal instruction (when you tell them the information). They may have problems with reading or writing and may often miss subtle facial or body language.

Visual: Visual learners learn best with visual teaching methods, such as photographs, drawings, and diagrams. Visual learners may have difficulty interpreting verbal instructions and need to have information written down (on their own and/or by others.) This group often see words in pictures.

Kinesthetic: Kinesthetic learners do best when they actually physically do the task (with their hands and/or bodies.) Role playing or participating in the process is their strength in learning.

The new Wechsler Intelligence Scale for Children-IV is now available and tests for Working Memory. Working Memory is the ability to hold something in short-term memory while doing some manipulation with it; for example, doing math problems in one's head, or writing an essay and forgetting what one is writing about.

Also, be aware that there are differences between I.Q. and achievement:

I.Q. (Wechsler Intelligence Scales for Children Revised) (WISC-R) looks at the child's potential.

Achievement (Wechsler Intelligence Achievement Test) (WIAT) looks at what the child is actually doing academically.

Executive functioning refers to the abilities that underline independent, purposeful, contextually appropriate behaviour.

As you can see, all of the information contained in the cognitive evaluations is vital information for parents as well as teachers because it indicates at what various levels your child is functioning and gives you the opportunity to teach to specific developmental and academic strengths. It also clarifies what your child's team (you, educators, coaches) should facilitate, such as more visual demonstration in teaching new concepts, supervision adjustments, or instruction of socialization skills curtailed to a more appropriate developmental age level.

For example, when we see a significant spread between the Verbal I.Q. and Performance I.Q., favoring the P.I.Q., it is anticipated that the patient will likely be frustrated and behaviours such as explosiveness and defensiveness are understandable. These patients' scores indicate that their visual and non-verbal abilities are much stronger than their language-based abilities. We need to examine how we speak to them: for example, did we use sentences that are too long, did we ask an abstract question, or did we confuse them with double-meaning words? If not, it periodically becomes difficult for us to determine what the trouble is, because they have so much difficulty communicating to us accurately what they want to say. Instead, it comes out in some form of reaction fuelled by their frustration. Imagine that you are talking, but no one can hear you, no matter how hard you try. Think of how that would feel. Would you be frustrated or aggravated; would you want to somehow get attention to be heard? Well, the situation involves all of that and more, which is why it is so important for us to look towards **our** actions first; perhaps we didn't realize that we might be part of the problem. By using concrete language, free of abstract concepts, and being aware of the length of our sentences we become part of the solution.

In the event testing has shown that your child has a weakness in Verbal I.Q. scores, I highly recommend this book: *When The Brain Can't Hear - Unravelling The Mystery Of Auditory Processing Disorder,* written by Teri James Bellis, Ph.D. It is an excellent resource with detailed explanations of learning, language and auditory processing.

For persons diagnosed with FASD, a wide range of I.Q. scores have been documented from the Intellectually Deficient range to Superior range. Although overall I.Q. is not always an accurate predictor of an individual's skills, it is a good idea to review the **scores** to provide a **general** sense of where they are in the universal population. In the event that the patient is in the Low Average, Borderline, or Intellectually Deficient range of overall functioning, this by **no means** reflects that there is no hope for success. In fact, once we acknowledge the special needs in terms of developmental age, as opposed to their chronological age, we are in the best position to offer the appropriate support at home or school and in community activities. Further, for those affected individuals that fall in the Average, High Average or Superior range, the overall I.Q. is **truly not** an accurate predictor of their skills, especially in daily living tasks, memory, and problem solving. It is typically the patients in these ranges of I.Q. that we would worry about the most, because their disabilities are so often disguised as intended behaviours. FASD affected people that fall within the range of Average to Superior Intelligence often present with more sophisticated behaviours and they may well have the ability to manipulate a situation to their advantage. However, these abilities often mask the real disability, which is evident in their executive or day-to-day functioning: They do not show up on time or at all, have problems following social rules incorporated in laws, cannot conceptualize that eight dollars is not enough to buy six months worth of food, or appreciate that sleeping is not likely a shrewd career goal. As a parent, go with your gut instinct in determining whether some of your child's behaviour is the disability talking or if he or she is just making an attempt at skirting a punishment. Disability or no disability, sometimes kids naturally try to yank your chain. Trust what you feel inside; just as in other areas of life, it will always serve you well.

Two main issues lead to misinterpretation of behaviour particularly for adolescents. Firstly, we may not fully comprehend the range and dimension of cognitive deficits due to the alcohol insult *in utero*. For example, an adolescent may be in the intellectually deficient range of functioning, but is not recognized as such by others because of his clever conversational skills. Conversely, another young person or adult may be in the Average to Superior range of I.Q., yet he or she is at a loss in executive or day-to-day functioning. In either case, there is an assumption that these patients are much higher functioning than they actually are in certain areas. Secondly, we tend to graduate independence for our teens based on their chronological age and not on their specific overall executive functioning capacity. For example, a sixteen-year-old boy is expected to make change at his job but in his particular situation, moneymaking skills have stagnated at a seven year old's ability. Although he makes his best attempt, ultimately he is fired because he is accused of stealing. Adding to this dilemma, it appears to be human nature that we expect more from taller, larger individuals, particularly in common sense problem solving: "You're a teenager, so you should be able to make the correct change." Since no two individuals are ever affected the same way, it is critical that supervision be curtailed specifically to the individual's overall executive functioning abilities. Be mindful that some areas of day-to-day living will have to be monitored more stringently.

In general, the physician and/or psychologist usually recommend that cognitive evaluations (Psycho-Educational Assessments) should be repeated intermittently as your child matures. It is often suggested that testing be completed prior to grade one; shortly before grade five, where educational systems begin teaching in abstract concepts (problem solving), particularly in mathematics; and at pre-high school. Evaluations are also required for some patients shortly before they reach legal adulthood. Check with the diagnostic physician and psychologist for assistance in planning for your child's needs, especially patients that might be eligible for disabilities funding programs at the year of emancipation (18, 19 or 21 years of age as deemed by province or state). This type of assessment should be concluded six to eight months prior to their coming of age birthday to ensure there are no gaps in the transition to adult support services.

Repeated cognitive assessments distinguish improvements, as well as recognize where some skills may have reached their full potential. It is with this guideline that we are then able to plan more accurately with regard to supervision, academics, living skills, and short and long-term planning. Do not be lulled into a false sense of security that when behaviours are improving and your child is following through with rules and expectations that they are ready to handle more independence. It is the external supports in the environment (supervision, reminders, transportation assistance) that are likely responsible for this success. To extensively increase these responsibilities will likely set them up for failure and risk a rapid deterioration of not only behaviours but self-esteem as well. This is not to suggest that you don't try. The way to know that you have expected too much of them, is if they crash. The difference is in appreciating that they tried and assuring them that it was not a failure on their part, rather than assuming that they just don't care. Although they may be adults, you still need to be realistic in estimating what level of supervision and support they will require throughout their life course.

By establishing this with your child as soon as possible, the better chance you have of long-term success.

Questions to ask the psychologist:

*When discussing these issues request that you be given examples.

What is my child's Full Scale I.Q. and is there a significant (big) difference between the Verbal I.Q. and Performance I.Q.? If so, what does that mean?

Is there a difference between my child's potential and what he or she is actually doing academically?

Do the subtests show strengths and weaknesses in my child's learning profile?

Do we need to concentrate on teaching basic academic functional skills (such as counting change, reading street signs)?

Ask about percentile ranks. (For example, a percentile rank of 48 means the child scored higher than 48% of his/her peers.)

What strategies can we use to make it easier for him/her given the abilities?

What areas should we focus on at home to strengthen some of my child's abilities?

When do you recommend (at what age) that my child be tested again and will you be available to complete that testing at that time?

Does my child meet any criteria for disabilities funding of any kind?

Is there a possibility that my child may be eligible (in your province or state) for disability funding when reaching adulthood?

Does my child meet the criteria for any school coding, and if so, what is it and what does it mean?

Could you help me prepare the **Abilities List!** for my child in language that we understand?

Now, with the assistance of your child's Psychologist, write out the strengths and weaknesses that were revealed in the cognitive assessment.

We will refer to this as the **Abilities List!**

Abilities List!

Strengths	**Weaknesses**
•	•
•	•
•	•
•	•
•	•
•	•
•	•
•	•
•	•
•	•
•	•
•	•
•	•

Chapter Six

The OBD (Organic Brain Dysfunction) Strategy Guide!

Eloquently put by a father of five: "We teach our kids how to be successful rather than count on them figuring it out by trial and error or by natural, logical consequences. I think that is what has made the difference for all of us in our family."

The first thing you may notice in this section is that the strategies are not broken down into chronological age groups. This is because, to best understand the nature of this disability, we need to *determine the approximate developmental age level* of a child's functioning in certain areas. Once the basic developmental stage of a specified area is established, we will *teach to that level of comprehension* and *customize your expectations proportionately*. Be aware that developmental stages vary somewhat, as some kids reach milestones or "what they should be doing" sooner and some later. You are not looking for exactness, just to be in the ballpark. For example, a 14 year old may have reading skills equivalent to a 17-year-old academic level, but her social and emotional skills (the way she understands, acts and responds in social situations or relationships) are comparable to an eight-year-old level. Our objectives are to teach by using her strengths (reading and visual learner), and appreciate that in the specific area of social skills we need to support her as best we can just as we would a child of much younger years (in this case, teach to an eight year old's level of understanding of the subject by using books and movies that contain relationship lessons). This is not to suggest that we will condescend to her, but we realize that this is her level of understanding in that particular area, and we will design strategies based on that information. If you're not sure, you can brush up on developmental stages by referring to books in Childhood Development, or get some assistance from a child psychologist to direct you. The ultimate goals here are to empower children, avoid the temptation to try and control them, keep their dignity intact, build self-esteem and find some humour at the end of the day.

Impulsivity, attention, distractibility and hyperactivity

- **Alert! Do not buy into media suggestions that "ADHD is the disability de'jour"** and "it is popular because it's an excuse for not getting things done." If your child has a confirmed diagnosis within the Fetal Alcohol Spectrum Disorder range with a secondary diagnosis of ADD or ADHD, trust me, he or she *has Attention Deficit Disorder*. It must be acknowledged as a medical condition, with or without medication. This kind of nonsense is comparable to what was interpreted and reported by the media years ago that child sexual abuse was "a new epidemic," and that many girls and boys were "misreading things" or, worse, "lying." The truth is, until we started asking the right questions, we didn't know how pervasive sexual assault of children really was. We know now that extensive numbers of people, male and female, were sexually and physically abused in residential care facilities and many of these individuals have since been publicly vindicated. ADD and ADHD are real and quite likely responsible for some major challenges for you and your child. Accepting it is the first step towards moving forward.

- **It is a personal choice of parents and later ADHD adults whether to medicate or not.** What you need is accurate information regarding today's medication, so ask your doctor and talk to other parents. You'll find that for some it has been very effective and for others it has been a disaster. If you choose alternatives to prescription medication, please be cautious. If you are considering medicating your child with herbal remedies, consult with a qualified professional! Herbal supplements can have adverse effects, and the quantity amounts and ratios are very difficult to judge. I notice that some of my older patients who do not feel comfortable on prescription medication drink gallons of coffee and other caffeine-laden products to keep afloat (sorry, bad pun). Others manage fairly well because they have families and/or partners that accept them for who they are, and utilize other methods of coping with attention problems, such as regimented organization, deep breathing and memory tricks. There is no right or wrong answer here. Medication is a choice that every family has to assess for themselves.

- If you are an organized person by DNA, then go on to the next paragraph. If you're not, and readily admit that you could be chosen to make an appearance on a reality game show that entails the clutter removal police coming to your house and filming you while you're sobbing over parting with a rusty cheese grater, listen up. **Being organized and learning to be organized is vital to you and your child's idyllic future.** It is a core life strategy you can give your child. Messiness creates a stressful environment for your child, and whether you know it or not, it may also be having a negative effect on you. Being organized allows you to feel more relaxed and literally helps clear your mind. If you don't know how or where to start, find someone who is a natural-born arranger (like the person that skipped this paragraph). Believe me, people that love to organize would be thrilled at the prospect of getting you and your family organized. "Control freaks" (for lack of a more endearing term) have a real advantage over those of us who don't possess such qualities and are happy to share their talent - it is what they do best! You know at least one of them, so find your Monica Gellar, take a deep breath and take the plunge. I learned my life strategies from the best in the west, a teacher of all ages for over 40 years who invented organizational tactics with SWAT team precision - my mom. She used to say, "Disorder in the room is disorder in the mind." Hmm, Attention Deficit *Disorder*. She may have been a little ahead of her time with that one. She would start by breaking a really big job into smaller ones: "Complete and then repeat!" For example, instead of "clean up your room," it would be "pick up all of the clothes that are on the floor and put them in the basket." When that was done, "Great! Now put all of the books on your bed on the shelf...." Complete and then repeat. Another one of my favourite strategies of hers was to have me choose big brightly coloured construction paper to write out my multiplication tables. The thought of doing mathematics would make me nauseous (still does); however, because I loved the colour turquoise it held my attention longer and made studying more bearable.

- **Encourage your child to find a special place that is not distracting *to him or her.*** Make it a space that is conducive not only to homework, but hobby activities, leisure reading or special things of interest such as poetry writing. This area should not be used for time-outs or consequences, because its purpose is to act as a sanctuary where your child can also go to relax or calm down if necessary. It is not recommended that this is done in a bedroom as there are far too many temptations (sometimes picking a watermelon-size hole in the wall from a paint chip is much more interesting than spelling practice sheets). Look around the house together, and find a feasible area that both of you are comfortable with; then let your imaginations take over. These spaces can be really entertaining to put together with your child, being mindful of lighting (many prefer halogen lamps) and low noise level. Experiment with seating such as beanbag chairs, drapes or netting to seclude the space. Try different textures of fabric that are appealing to their senses. If your child enjoys aromas, it's a perfect place to set up an aromatherapy pot; one scent to stimulate the brain for homework and another for relaxation! These types of "rooms" do not need to be expensive, as proved by one little guy who hauled an old refrigerator box out of the garage, insisting it was perfect for his "Space" - Space. He and his dad spent an enjoyable Saturday morning cutting out the top; they placed a swing-armed halogen lamp over top, which floods a soft light downwards. They painted it (he chose all black with small blue-white stars). They topped it off with a foam chair that they bought at a garage sale, and he and his dad built a custom-made tabletop with left over plywood. His mom covered the chair with fun-fur that he chose after touching and feeling nearly every bolt in the fabric shop! Nonetheless, he loves it, uses it, and has a sense of accomplishment that he designed and helped build it.

- For things that children really need to pay attention to, **you'll attract and hold their concentration better if you refer to them by their name and make direct eye contact.** For all of you tall people that means *their* eye level, as opposed to them staring at your navel.

- **Currently our society is inundated with relaxation products and activities, but strangely we do not seem to focus on teaching children or persons with disabilities to relax.** In a life where they have to think harder than others, deal with constant confusion not knowing what they've done wrong, being physically tired purely due to the arrangement of their body parts, it seems that this population would benefit the most from regular relaxation time. With the surmounting tension of daily living, teach your child, your family and yourself to relax. You could all use it and it's fun. Creative therapies such as art therapy, breathing/stretching relaxation techniques, aroma therapy, yoga, running, massage, bubble baths and dimmer switches in the bathroom, tai chi, meditation, hanging up side down for a while, are just to name a few. Incorporate a relaxation routine *at least* once a day, and decide what time of day would be most beneficial. Many kids have a routine as soon as they get home from school, when they're tighter than a drum, or before bed when it is hard for them to settle into sleep. Some families have a routine together, so experiment and find what works for you and your child. *Please make sure to have your doctor approve the plan, as some things may be hazardous to health.* Give your child the option to give relaxation time a name, and you can do the same to make it more personally inspiring. (I mistakenly named mine "happy hour" when I had my two small nieces over for summer holidays. Every day at four o'clock, we would have our choice of drinks: Rachel loved Mountain Dew and Ali was a Cream Soda fanatic; and snacks were served as well, always Pringles and Cheese Nachos respectively. I managed to eat and drink both. Come fall, Ali started school, and when asked what she had done in the summer, she gleefully told her classmates (and teacher) that she most enjoyed her Aunt Lizzie's "Happy Hour" which consisted of "drinking, eating and a lot of laughing." Needless to say, I had some explaining to do to with my sister-in-law.

- **Get those backpacks cleaned out.** Honestly, we've got kids in grade one resembling tiny airline attendants that need wheels on their backpacks to schlep all this stuff to and from school. Little wonder kids today are stressed out. Organization techniques like sorting, throwing out, keeping for tomorrow and figuring out what needs to be attended to (e.g. a homework assignment or field trip release form) must be instilled as a daily ritual, not just when something starts to smell.

- **Gear new activities towards things that you're pretty sure they might be good at.** Recently I tried Pilates. I'm not quite sure what I was thinking because it requires paying strict attention for over 38 seconds *and* doing two things at once. The point is I never went back because I was a klutz at it, and I felt bad that I couldn't do it like all the others. For things that children do not eventually pick up or seem to enjoy, try something different, not force them to try harder. People with attention problems tend to have less "stick-to-it-ness" because of the helter-skelter way their minds work; they get bored quickly and move onto the next thing. In our society we place a great deal of emphasis on finishing what we start, and view not seeing things through as a weakness. Then again, lots of very successful entrepreneurs tried a million things before they found the one idea that hit the jackpot even when others said they would never amount to anything. Believe in children, not their actions!

- **If you have established that your child is easily over stimulated, do a "disarray check" in his or her bedroom.** See if there is anything that can be taken out or reorganized that might be acting as a distraction at bedtime or interfering in getting ready for school. Today's children typically have a lot of "stuff," and much of it they might not even miss. Evaluate whether wall murals, mobiles, televisions, computers, 10,000 Polly Pockets, books, videos, DVD's, CD's, or the entire stuffed animal kingdom are better to be removed. Involve children in the process - *slowly* and *not* as a consequence. Let them choose one thing first and *show them where it is going* (like the basement or garage), and let them help. Have them participate in a charity donation, where they can see that other less fortunate children could re-use and enjoy the same toys that they have outgrown, or have them participate in a garage sale. Believe me, FASD or not FASD - money talks. If your spouse still owns a high-school jean jacket and an assortment of single socks, you may want to include them in this conversation with your other children.

- **Adapt to the times and take a look at reading products** like Leap Pad ® (the Amazing Spiderman for 1st Grade) and other computer options that are at geared at visual, auditory and participatory learning. Have your child teach you a few tricks on the computer, as he or she might be able to put together your next PowerPoint presentation! (Warning: The last kid that did this for me programmed my laptop to sound like a dolphin, and I can't get it off! - funny guy.) In the same breath I'm also going to suggest that the computer age, though it has brought some excellent options in education, has also created a new era of complete stimulus overload. It is time to find a balance! In many cases, we don't even notice until we *consciously* pay attention to it. What did we ever do before cell phones, pagers, computer games and fax machines? For starters, it was a lot quieter everywhere and we actually had five minutes to ourselves. Check out how much "computer-age" noise is relevant to your family; don't forget that a barrage of flashing lights on a screen can be *subtly* annoying, and still a form of commotion. Inspect your home to see if stimulation overload may be secretly penetrating your family, and regulate it accordingly.

- **Begin deep breathing exercises (both of you) right before starting something that the individual anticipates is going to be challenging.** Physical relaxation is imposed on the body when we inhale through the nose slowly, and deeply breathe out through the mouth. This will not only reduce excess stress but will also clarify the mindset enhancing the success of the attempt. It works - try it out, too!

- **Things are going to get lost - count on it, plan for it and anticipate it.** Make duplicate copies of identification (maybe quadruplicate on that one), day-timers, work schedules, winter jackets, retainers, mittens, eyeglasses, lunch bags, CD's, wedding rings, toothbrushes, etc., etc., etc.

- **Ensure regular bathroom breaks** because some children get busy and forget to go. Sometimes they'll be so stuck on an activity that they wait a little too long, and then it's "all over but the crying," so to speak.

- **Limit homework to a reasonable amount of time,** especially if it is becoming too wearisome. Chances are it is going to take your child longer to do homework, so keep the lines of communication open with the school staff. Further, depending on the extent of your child's learning disabilities, he or she may require a professional tutor (not with the kid next door who aced science). Talk to the teacher at that time about what can be cut down of the curriculum, and/or discuss whether another program would be more suitable to your child's needs. Investigate funding possibilities to hire a professional tutor through Social Services Agencies, your doctor, or FASD support groups. Don't be shy to get the help you need; that is what they are there for and are most often happy to help.

- **Sometimes a heavy comforter, to "weight" them down from the "hyper-ness"** or wound up feeling, can prove helpful for those with difficulty settling into sleep. It can also be effectively used to crawl under when they are feeling over-stimulated at other times of the day. This is the same theory for the weighted vests for daytime. Be sure to have any homemade versions checked out by an Occupational Therapist and/or Physiotherapist so that these will not inadvertently cause bodily problems.

- For children from traditional Native families, **ceremonial sweats are an excellent way** to blend spirituality and healing into a relaxation technique.

Memory, abstraction and sequencing

- **Tip: If it means something TO YOU, you'll have a better chance of remembering it.** I was once explaining to a dad how his son's memory deficit was causing academic and seemingly defiant behaviour problems. He glared at me and quickly snapped, "Listen, lady, there is nothing wrong with his memory - if I tell him that we are going to MacDonald's three weeks from Thursday, THAT he'll remember!" Well, sure. It's probably *all* he thought about because it is his favourite place to go, eat and play. It meant something **to him**, whereas if he was told to get on the bus at three p.m. and he was playing the lead in "Darth Vader Returns to the schoolyard," it might not manufacture the same interest level and subsequent follow through.

- **To effectively deal with your child's memory problems, concentrate on how he or she learns best.** Is it hearing the information, writing it out after a verbal direction, or hands-on experience, watching, demonstrating, visuals (pictures, diagrams), or a combination of these? Use children's strengths to help them transfer new information into long-term memory.

- *Do not just* **repeat, repeat, repeat. Show, tell, repeat.** Show, tell, repeat. Show, tell, repeat. Show, tell, repeat. Show, tell, repeat. Show, tell, repeat.

- **Make sure that your child understands the basic concept before starting on memorization techniques.** When trying out new games/sports, make sure children understand the rules and what they are supposed to do *before* they begin. If not, just be prepared to start running across four fields at break-neck speed after your kid gets possession of the soccer ball and is destined for home. Use visuals such as models, diagrams or outlines along with the verbal direction (show, tell, repeat). It is **really important** that you have **your child choose, create, draw or design the visual** as much as possible; in going through the process, he or she will have a much better chance of remembering it. Do it the way you see in the big leagues, drawing on a white board, or better yet with actual players. Drawing a picture is one of the best memory strategies you can provide.

- **Personalize the lessons as much as possible using their name, interests or things that are already familiar to them.** If they're into hair products, include these into the intended lesson as much as possible; for example, an innovative mathematics problem to solve: "If there is a sale on hair mousse at $2.39 each and you have five dollars, how many mousses could you buy?" If it is of interest to them, they'll be more apt to participate and retain the information.

- **Some kids are quite adept at reading body language and social cues** (when someone smiles or frowns at you, you respond accordingly). Others have great difficulty due to the depletion of cause-and-effect thinking abilities, and as a result the behaviour will look like they don't care how their actions impact other people. This is often why some individuals have short, tumultuous friendships and such difficulty at socializing - they don't get how their actions may have affected someone else. Take a lot of photographs of people, places and things, and teach them how to take pictures. Now, with digital cameras, this strategy is more accessible than ever. Have them take photographs of happy faces, mad faces, and bored faces, and have them identify these. Be careful that they don't make a "Mom's a Mad Maniac Mural" for the living room wall with their selections. Recently, I asked a mom in front of her teenage son if she had any previous photographs of him not smiling (for medical evaluation), to which he quipped, "That's probably all of them!" Let them experiment with photography to see where it leads them!

- **Here's a bold idea - *ask them* if they find one way of remembering easier than another.** I learned this lesson from a young lady who once said to me, "Why do you keep wanting me to write it just because I have good printing? I remember it better when I doodle a picture." Often we are so busy problem solving, organizing, planning, creating structure, routine and predictability, that we forget that kids may already have figured out their own strategies that seem to work best for them.

- **Have them practice looking at visuals to help them remember verbal information.** Tell them to look at an object, close their eyes and say what the object is out loud.

- **Allow the use of a palm pilot** - the one where they come home with their homework agenda written in ink on the inside of their hand. They have a slightly less chance of losing it as opposed to the other kind. Although the look of messy blue hands may arouse your natural instinct to scrub them raw, remember - it's not how you get there, it's how you end up. If it works for them, invest in a good hand cleaner to wipe the slate clean for the next encryption.

- **Memory games are fun for all ages especially if you get creative.** Make up your own games. For example, dig out family photos and place them upside down on a table. Everyone takes a turn flipping the picture over, looking at the image, and placing it back on the table upside down. Have your child recall memories attached to the pictures: "Which photo was taken when Uncle Jason fell in the lake?" Other variations could be using pictures of things of specific interest to your child, such as sports cards. This type of strategy can also be used as a study technique where the auditory (verbal) questions are asked; they have to find a correlating picture, and then say and write down an answer.

- **Some of us seem to remember things better in song or by rhyming.** Have them choose a favourite tune and write their own lyrics to assist them in not only remembering but getting organized. For example, remembering the phone number 589-8270 might be easier to remember as **5-8-9-8-270**! This can be very effective with adolescents in day-to-day routines, but also as a creative study technique. Of course, you may have to listen to rap more often, but you'll get over it when you see their report card.

- **Play the rumour game!** Put together a group and get into a circle. A sentence is written down and the object is to whisper it to the next person (not showing the paper). When it comes to the original player, he or she adds more words or a sentence and repeats the sequence. At the end, the last person has to say what he or she heard out loud to see how close it is to the original. It's a blast!

- Many children of all ages like to write or tell stories or poems. **Give them a head start by having them write down the major idea.** Then make points below, asking what happens first, next, then next? Then cut and paste the story together in the correct sequence. This can be done on computer or on paper. Another way to encourage writing is by having them experiment with different sizes and fonts on the computer to create a very professional look to their finished work. Frame it, laminate it, or get their work made up into a book with coil binding as a keepsake of their work. It is bound to inspire other creations.

- **Practice spelling by verbally spelling out the word**

and have them repeat it. It is helpful to do this with words that they already know and then gradually add new words and review.

- **Be prepared that grade-five mathematics may pose particular difficulty for them even if they have excelled in previous years.** It is no coincidence that a vast number of FASD patients encounter a shift in understanding as the grade five curricula introduce abstract concepts and problem solving. Some kids may experience difficulty in this area due to their particular type of brain dysfunction. For example, the teacher stands at the head of the class and announces that they will be starting problem solving and gives them a verbal description of the problem. "There is a dresser with three drawers. In each drawer there are two pairs of socks. How many pairs of socks are in the dresser?" You've lost them at "there is a dresser." By this time they may have determined that their teacher is delusional, as they scour the room trying to find this supposed dresser that she is talking about. Again, abstract concepts are things you cannot see - in this case there is no dresser to see or touch. Have your child draw out the problem by making a picture of a dresser with the drawers and socks inside, and presto, the correct answer!

- **Persons who have problems with abstract concepts sometimes have problems deciphering longhand writing.** It is very helpful to them to have directions set out in printing. As affected persons do not grow out of their disabilities, this technique is applicable to adults as well.

- **Thousands of kind-hearted FASD individuals have given away their play-stations, or their entire pay cheques, to those they thought needed it more.**

The concept of value is abstract. Practice with things that you agree are okay to give to a person in need, and be very clear about items that are not for charity, like your new motor home. Another way to reinforce this concept is to actually show them the cash it takes to replace the item (put them side by side) and give them a visual comparison to the money they get for allowance or working. In some cases you may have to restrict accordingly the amount of money they carry on a daily basis.

- **Be patient and give them a minute to digest the information.** Some patients take longer than others to process and think things through. Pause for a couple of seconds at the end of a sentence or paragraph depending on their abilities, and then check whether they understood by asking them a question related to the information. If they are not able to answer in their own words, that is your cue to either slow down or determine whether they need a different type of assistance such as breaking it down into smaller steps or using a visual aid.

- **Try to be clear and concise when giving instructions.** Be mindful of using too many words or droning on in a lecture about inappropriate behaviour. Use clear, consistent language to provide children with clear concrete signals to help them remember and combine language with visual cues to reinforce the message. If you carry on chastising them for not remembering their homework for 28 minutes with compelling eye contact, and then ask whether they understood, you're more apt to get a response like "did you know you have more eyelashes on one eye than the other?" Shorten it up and you're going to get greater results, feel better, and have more time to do something nice for yourself!

- **If they are stronger in Auditory Memory** (words said to them), have them talk out loud and rehearse verbally what they need to remember.

- **Have them make an acronym for information that they will need to recall**, for example, an exam. An acronym is the letters that stand for companies, organizations, associations or terms that are used in computer email language, like LOL, which stands for "Laughing out loud" or "SNAP (Special Needs Adoptive Parents.)" The important thing to remember is to have **them** devise or assist them in creating an acronym, as they will have a much better chance of remembering it.

- **Get them into the habit of using visuals to help with remembering how to get places;** teach them to use landmarks (which don't move, like a building) when going to and from school or to and from a job.

- **Including children or teens in grocery shopping is a great way to get them to practice list making while recognizing that items are placed in categories and sequences.** For instance, all soups are together, meats, vegetables and so on. Older kids may be asked to make up a short grocery list and follow through with the order. Some children find it easier to have a picture or label of the item to remind them, with the written description next to it. Don't forget, it is important to let them devise their own strategy for recall: this might be drawing an illustration or mapping that they create themselves. It is never too early to start teaching life skills.

- **When introducing new concepts, make a connection between the new information and information they already know.**

- For things they really need to remember that seem hard for them, have them think up a reward for themselves that is reasonable to you both. Sometimes the actual retaining of information can act as the reward itself; for example, have them congratulate themselves when they have managed to remember, even if you've helped them: "I remembered to take my bathing suit, so I get to go swimming!"

- It is helpful to assist them in memory by teaching them to sort things by their similarities like size, texture, shapes or patterns on a day-to-day basis. Sorting laundry can be a fun way to practice: "How many blue t-shirts do you have? How many have a v-neck, a round neck? How many have short sleeves? Which one is the softest? Etc."

- Offer them the opportunity to teach a younger child or a friend to reinforce information that they have recently learned. Overall, kids like to help, and if they are given some sense of authority and credibility in educating others, it is more likely going to stick with them. Even the surliest of individuals will be helpful if they think it is all their idea (another husband parallel).

- Explore whether the subject matter at hand has been produced on video or DVD. Watching the movie *Romeo and Juliet*, while reading along, can be much more conducive to your teen's learning style than struggling through the book alone. It is not cheating; it's *learning*.

- Eliminate irrelevant information from instructional conversation and in written instructions. When reading, have them highlight the key words that capture the main subject of the paragraph or what they actually need to retain. Then have them talk about why they chose the word and how it helps them remember the rest of the information. Be prepared because they may have a tendency to pick an area of interest to them and not the main idea, as they have a different pattern of recall. To review, have them go back to the words or phrase that they highlighted; then have them discuss what they remember and why. Ask questions related to the story to ensure they are comprehending the words and not just reading them. We can assist them by showing them how to link the information together in order. It can be helpful to do this by including a "study-buddy" so that a friend can use the same strategy, and then they can help each other.

- **Routine is a gift to a person with memory problems.** It helps them to do things in a predictable sequence and, because routine is repetition, it is what most enhances the memory.

- **Prepare them for attending school whether it is for the first time or changing grades.** Transitions to a new classroom, new teacher, new classmates and new daily routine are stressful particularly when one is not able to anticipate what to expect. Request that your child have a "walk through" when the school is not full of other children. Help children draw a map of where to go and have them practice a couple of times to find their classroom, bathroom and coat rack. If possible, request that your child's coat hanger be at the end rather than the middle to avoid potential over-stimulation problems. For children graduating to higher grades such as junior or senior high school, this process is even more necessary as students are expected to find gymnasiums, lockers, the office and bathrooms on their own. Don't be afraid to request a specific location for their locker such as the end of the row or in close proximity to classes. If it makes it easier for them it will reduce their anxiety and avoid trouble. In grades where there are options for certain classes, encourage children to sign up for a session where they have strengths and enjoy the subject. For example, they could take a poetry, construction, art or cooking class as a means of relaxation and stress management. (Schedule at the end of the day if possible). Again, speak to the school staff privately about offering your teenager the opportunity to have a "guided tour" before school starts and when a staff member is available. See if another student may be able to help. It's a great way for them to feel more at ease and independent, and they may make a new friend!

- **Teach them to repeat instructions to themselves** and experiment with rhythm and rhymes.

- **Traditional Native beadwork is a terrific way to practice sequencing skills** as they are repeating colour sequences, for example, blue, blue, red, white.

- **Realize that your child will likely require re-teaching and repetition.** Count on it and try making it as much fun for you as for her or him. Reward **yourself** for your efforts in teaching new skills - whether it is a chocolate bon-bon, a new magazine, or a fishing rod. Take a break to pat yourself on the back for *your* job well done.

- **Always try to end on a positive note when using any strategy.** Innately we are drawn to things that made us feel good.

- **If children are not partial to games that contain**

themes and ideas (such as house, doctor, dolls, tractor pull or cashier), it is very possible that they may have trouble processing sequencing, order and logic. It is helpful to get them started by getting down on the floor and showing them the steps: ask them questions (who is this?) and follow through on their responses (that is the mommy doll). Create a story (sequencing), be sure to introduce the next steps (in order), and have it make sense (logic).

- **Make a pizza together.** You heard me. What better way to teach sequencing than to get out the ingredients on a Saturday night and put them on in order? Crust, sauce, cheese, toppings, cook, yummo! That's teaching a sequence! Better yet, buy them a children's cookbook and have them follow the directions. Use a pencil to check off each step when it is completed. Some of us have been known to create some pretty unsavoury dishes because we forgot that we had already added one teaspoon of salt, and then did it again! Learning to cook teaches not only sequencing but organizational skills, and is a self-esteem booster as well. Best of all, it's fun and they are rewarded for their efforts with a tasty treat for the entire family to enjoy.

Problem solving

- **Problem solving requires the abilities to compare, contrast, weigh and evaluate information that is already stored in our memory bank.** It is the process of retrieving that information, bringing it forward to the here and now, and then making a decision based on that information. From that, we derive cause-and-effect thinking: "If I do this - this will happen." For patients whose brain dysfunction has compromised these abilities, there is a problem with problem solving.

- **Encourage list making.** It's fast, cheap and effective. Teach list making from the time they can stand on their own. Help them make a TO DO LIST in the evening for things to be accomplished the next day. Do not make the list too long, make sure the objectives on the list are obtainable and include something enjoyable (not just mundane assignments). Fool around with different mediums on which to write the TO DO LIST, like on brightly coloured or shaped Post-It notes, or find one with their name already written on the top at a novelty shop! Review the list first thing in the morning as a reminder, and have them cross off items as they go. If they forget to cross things off, have them do it that evening, and praise them for their accomplishment. Rewrite a new list that evening, and include the jobs that did not get done; be careful to add to the list without making it overwhelming. It is an excellent way to assist them in learning a viable life strategy, and it gives you a built-in red flag if there is an area that requires more support. If there is a certain item that is consistently not getting done, investigate the possibilities why. Then put in the supports that will make it achievable; for example, they may need a telephone call to remind them in the day if you are not there.

- **A terrific approach for problem solving is to have them draw out a "Pros and Cons" list, even at a young age.** Take a sheet of paper, half it and get them to write out the benefits and downfalls in their own language (example, plus-side + and minus-side -). It's a great way for them to *actually see* the number of positives in comparison with negatives in order to make a good decision. Another model I use is the Plan A, Plan B that is designed the same way, with a line splitting a piece of paper down the middle. It assures that if Plan A doesn't work out, we have a Plan B, which can considerably reduce their stress level if they know that there is something to fall back on. Make it a habit to "sugar-up" the Plan B in some way so that if Plan A doesn't work out they have something to look forward to and don't interpret the disappointment as a total defeat.

- **Do the "Multiple Choice Extravaganza!" game.** It has proved to be a very effective strategy in practicing solving problems of all kinds. For example, sitting in the kitchen, while Dad is making dinner, you write on a piece of paper to your daughter:

"Do you think I should help Dad with dinner?" and provide three choices for her to check off the answer:

❏ Yes, his cooking stinks
❏ No, he cooks better than you
❏ Let's both help him so we can eat sooner

Bear in mind, regardless of their answer, it is the *process* of solving a problem we are teaching, not necessarily the content. By offering ways to solve the problem, children can manage an answer that gives them a giggle and keeps their dignity intact. Have you ever been put on the spot in a game where you didn't know the answer when everyone else is rolling their eyes? At least if you have a choice, you've got a better shot at the right answer and are more willing to continue playing and learning from the game. The point of this diversion is to get them to participate in an amusing but useful approach to making good choices for themselves. Reverse the order by letting them make up the question or problem and think up three answers. If you start out with the humorous rendition, they are much more likely to use the same strategy for more serious matters down the road. It's a great stress-buster while you're waiting for dinner to cook, waiting for an appointment, or handling a more delicate conversation!

- **Visually list limited, concrete and simple rules.** These have to be **consistent** in the household. That means that the caregivers are *in agreement* ahead of time and if not, skip to Chapter 7. When in disagreement, take a good look at your child's overall executive functioning and err on the side of caution for now. If the rules are not working, identify why they are not working based on your new assessment of your child's abilities, and act accordingly. Is it that he or she is not able to handle more responsibility and has cratered to prove it? Are your expectations realistic? Make sure that the rules in your house are reasonable and based on your child's overall functioning abilities and not necessarily chronological age. When children approach adolescence, it might be helpful to include them in setting rules and limits so that they feel that they are heard and part of the decision-making process. Negotiate, if possible, because it gives them a sense of empowerment and some control. As with all teenagers, we need to know where they are *at all times* to ensure their safety and, more than ever, reduce the opportunity for them to fall into a "wrong crowd." It takes a lot of work to monitor your child's comings and goings; but, I cannot state this more emphatically, it is much easier to prevent alcohol, drug or sexual experimentation than to unravel it once it has become a fascination and part of their lifestyle.

- **Getting dressed on their own may pose some problem-solving dilemmas for some affected**

individuals. Parents have addressed this in a number of inventive ways. A favourite is using "hockey hangers" (where you can hang an entire outfit) so that you and/or your child can create outfits ahead of time that include everything from shirts to socks, and simply pull it out of the closet and voila - dressing time is reduced to mere seconds! Actually pasting pictures of the items stored inside each drawer in a chest makes finding underpants, t-shirts, etc. easy for even little ones to become more self-sufficient. Wire or clear plastic baskets are also great ideas to store smaller clothing items for quick, visual access. If you live in a variable climate where your child needs to consider dressing for temperature at different times of the year, make it a seasonal event to put away all their winter, spring, fall or summer clothing (in the basement or under the bed) to reduce the chance of an inappropriate choice. To assist them in determining winter clothing, hang an outside thermometer with a bright line that indicates to wear extras such as heavier socks, hats, mittens or sweaters.

- **The game of golf is a spectacular way to teach and practice a number of skills in this area and more.** (Manners and etiquette are a must in this game.) My husband and I once golfed with a man and son who was observably brain injured. Nonetheless, he was a proficient and confident golfer and knew the rules better than we did! You never know what kids will grab onto and who knows, you may be playing with the next Tiger Woods!

Communication skills

- **Teach them to use affirmation statements.** The power of suggestion is an untapped goldmine for anyone, but particularly for persons that have trouble with assertion. For instance, ever notice sometimes when you are carrying a full tray and someone says, "You're going to drop it," then sure enough, you drop it? It is the same concept as telling children that they are not capable; they will subsequently respond as incompetent. Squelch the "can't do's" and pump up the "can do's." Help them to believe in themselves by having them develop self-empowerment statements like "I am a great diver and a nice friend." Once they get the hang of it, they can use this method to approach the goals they set out for themselves, such as starting the September of a challenging grade twelve year with "I am graduating in June, soon!"

- **Find their pace in how they digest information, and gear your directions according to their speed.** This is not to suggest that we speak in slow motion if a child needs more time in between steps, directions, questions or sentences; rather, just smoothly follow their tempo.

- **Encourage them to answer questions and take risks even if it is a guess.** Give them positive reinforcement even if they have the wrong answer, as in "That was a great try!" This is particularly important for children with auditory processing problems because it gives them more confidence to use their verbal skills.

- **Ensure that your child comprehends what has been asked by using visual aids, diagrams, pictures or actual demonstration.** When children are not following through correctly, it is very tempting to ask them to repeat back the instructions verbatim, but that does not verify whether they actually understood or not. Ask them to tell you in their own words to ensure they comprehended the direction accurately. If they can't do it, re-phrase the sentence. For patients with weak verbal reasoning skills this approach may promote even more frustration because they have such difficulty putting ideas in words. **Learn to talk so they understand you.** Check how you actually explained the information and evaluate whether you might have used idiomatic language or words that have two meanings. Did you use too many words or steps at a time? Some patients have decoding problems when they "hear" or process only every third word of the entire sentence. Perhaps you have used an abstract word or concept that needed a visual cue attached to it? For example, in the phrase "watch for mistakes," *watch* has two meanings: (1) a wristwatch that makes blunders or (2) to observe and make corrections. In order for them to understand the concept of "observation" you need to use a visual demonstration. Remember, things you cannot actually see in the here and now are abstract concepts. If you have a concrete thinker on your hands, point to the page or object and show what you are talking about.

- **If children are *stronger* in Verbal skills than Performance skills, it may be helpful to let them answer questions verbally.** Let them talk out their answers, and if necessary, request a scribe (a person to read the instructions aloud), or have them use a Dictaphone for written assignments. This way it will help them to correct themselves, and/or give you an opportunity to hear where they are veering off in the wrong direction, and intervene when needed.

- **In this day and age, it is beneficial to have your child learn appropriate keyboarding** (what we used to call typing) skills, rather than relying on the standard "hunt and peck." Children can then complete assignments more quickly and with less frustration on the computer. It also helps their self-esteem to turn in work that looks professional if they are cursed with very awkward penmanship due to their motor skills.

- **Reading skills can be strengthened by having a special person (grandmother, girlfriend/boyfriend, teacher) make a book tape** for your child; then have the child read the book while listening to the voice on a headset attached to a tape recorder. It has proven to be a very effective strategy as the child/teen chose the person, and it holds his or her attention longer.

- **Even if your child's reading skills are weak, practice, practice, practice** with comics, magazines, newspaper, book tapes, books, cereal boxes, or the fine print you can't read on the menu. Regardless of the extent of the disability, the goal is to **teach basic functional reading skills** to enable and empower them in adulthood.

- **Play word games such as Scrabble, Spill n' Spell and try out Word Find and Crosswords books.** I have one patient who at 12 is at the MENSA or "brainiac" level in puzzle solving! Also explore as many computer programs that involve creative language skill building as you can; borrow from the library or ask a teacher, psychologist or language specialist for advice.

- **Some kids will use a lot of chatter to disguise their lack of knowledge or understanding in the subject of the conversation.** They may also argue about a small thing to distract you from knowing that they do not understand. At this point try not to get into it with them because, if coupled with perseveration behaviours (not being able to let something go), you could be there until next Thursday. Be sure that others know that your child's strengths are masking serious difficulty with language processing, verbal reasoning and comprehension, because those difficulties all relate to behaviour, learning and social skills within the community.

- **Aboriginal "Talking sticks or feathers" are used in some groups, and the person holding the stick has a turn to speak and then passes it on.** It teaches many things such as taking turns, respecting others and process. It is a terrific visual aid that is most helpful for affected individuals to know when to talk and when to listen.

- **Use clear, concise and concrete words to assist them in how to verbally identify what has provoked an inappropriate behaviour:** "I didn't want to get off the computer, but you made me and then I got mad." A young man that was in a job interview demonstrated a great example of this recently: "You are speaking too fast and that confuses me. Could you please slow down?" Later, the interviewer indicated that she hired him because she was impressed by his courage to communicate.

- **Enlist someone else to relay information** that your adolescent refuses to talk to you about. It is a completely normal phenomenon that teenagers think that their parents are completely stunned and that they know better, so if they'll listen to an aunt, or family friend, terrific. Just make sure that the individual is aware of any processing problems and adjusts their conversation accordingly. It may also be a good idea to have the liaison go over basically what was talked about with you and your teenager to avoid a "did not, did so" conversation and make sure everyone is on the same page.

- **Secret code words or signals to communicate** are a playful and effective way for all ages to approach a potential powder-keg discussion. Naturally, most of us become slightly defensive when someone else is offering some "constructive criticism" regardless of the topic. It stands to reason that kids can get pretty sick and tired of perpetual verbal corrections to their actions. In "teachable time," or in other words when everyone is in a good mood, discuss the option of them coming up with a code word or hand signal that gingerly reminds them which action (behaviour) could use a tune-up. It is important that **your child** chooses the word or signal (expect a certain universal hand gesture at some point) that gives a cue to knock it off. One mom approached her son about him getting over-stimulated and "silly" when other people were around, so to circumvent the problem he came up with the code word "George," which is his short version of George of the Jungle. I know what you're thinking, and yes, he does have a fantastic sense of self-awareness for six. Now when he's getting a bit loud or soon to be spinning out of control, his mom asks, "George, would you like an apple?" It is a gentle hint for him to calm down, and he does, with dignity.

Soft neurological signs

- **Play detective and find the connection between their behaviour and an over-stimulation problem.** For example, do they start to get anxious, act up or start pushing in a crowd? If so, that is your clue that they are not able to handle line-ups, noisy places and crowds. Taper down the opportunity of them being in such situations, and it will in turn reduce the incidence of those behaviours. Lots of people don't like crowds and typically will steer clear of them, even parties or events of interest. Your child might be one such, so she or he may need your help to avoid places that would be difficult to handle, for example, attending a lengthy church service or shopping on Boxing Day. It just might not be worth the upset for your child or you. Always keep in the back of your mind that the behaviour is harder for your child to control once already immersed in an over-stimulating environment, so choose carefully.

- **Blackout time. When they're getting really over-stimulated, have them close or cover their eyes,** use a night mask, have them crawl under a big blanket, or zip up in a sleeping bag for a few minutes to regain composure. Sometimes even the slightest movement or flickering of a television can be extremely aggravating. In a high stress time, these are economical, easy and efficient life strategies that they could use to ease tension and calm anxiety.

- **Lots of people with central nervous system disruption do not feel at home in their own bodies.** It is like having a perpetual sense of internal uneasiness. Sometimes they are muscularly tense, and this can be thoroughly compounded by having a really bad day. Their movements can be chaotic and abrupt. To help them, experiment with sensory experiences involving taste, such as trying different consistencies and flavours of foods; for example, crunchy snacks may release some tension. Test various textures on the skin like bubble baths, flannel sheets or a silk comfort pillow. Remove all clothing tags from the nape of the neck and back of the pants, and try clothing made of cottons (which breathe and are soft) or micro-fibre. Venture into what seems to suit them best like cold or warm sensations for relaxation. Some kids find a cold shower invigorating while others prefer a hot bath. Try eye-gel packs (cold or hot) or herbal teas served in a pretty teacup that they received for their birthday. Other suggestions include a professional massage, aromatherapy, stretching, laying down with a scented pillow, trampoline antics (with a really big net around it!), pushing or pulling heavy objects, running, or popping a hundred feet of bubble paper. The sky is the limit!

- **Some children and youth have difficulty with visual-spatial abilities;** they find it nearly impossible to copy things, and many have trouble with hand-eye coordination as well. Games like puzzles (available for all ages), Lego, blocks, models of cars or ships, hand-sewing, embroidery or knitting all may boost skills in this area. If they find it way too frustrating, move onto something else. We don't need to sew our own clothes anymore, so it's not a big deal if it's not their forte.

- **Personal space and social boundaries:** I know a man (who will remain nameless) who will seek out an aisle at the grocery store and park himself directly in front of a lady who is already in the midst of making a soup decision. He continues to block her view until eventually she turns to me and enquires, "Do you think I should use my powers of invisibility to fight crime or for evil?" He has no clue. Of course I use the oldest method of cueing him to his error by grabbing the back of his pants and twirling him around to get the visual cue - he is in her space. Some folks have limited to no instinctive sense or feeling of the space around them. A way to clarify this is to actually show them by demonstrating an arm's length and reminding them that it is the appropriate space between them and another person. Then practice, practice, and practice. Experiment with using a visual guideline like making a box out of masking tape on the floor to define a space they need to stay in to get work done. Over time it will help them adapt to the space that is expected for others to feel comfortable.

- **For a child or youth with poor fine motor skills, try a heavier lead pencil** or pen with a larger grip, heavier cutlery for mealtimes. (It often looks as if children are holding their fork with a fist). Experiment with different types of utensils so your child can find one that works best for him or her. Dollar stores are famous for all kinds of neat stuff to write with that is not too expensive. Don't worry about the neatness of handwriting and focus more on legibility. Be innovative: wrapping presents and tying bows, and playing catch with one hand are great ways of strengthening fine motor skills! Contact your local Physiotherapist and Occupational Therapist for more strategies specifically designed to your child's special needs.

- Most of us would look forward to a day at the beach, but for some children who have **heightened skin (touch) sensitivities** to hats, grass, sand and salt water, it may be so irritating to them that it could be a recipe for disaster. On the upside, for the little ones with no speech that can't tell you what's wrong, the high-pitched screeching has a good chance of beckoning a pod of whales, so the whole day isn't entirely shot. Bring a large umbrella, big cotton blanket or sheet to make a large play space, tap water to cool them down, and supply favourite toys that can entertain them while you bask in the sun!

- On the other hand, for kids that love and/or eat dirt, **get them out gardening. Not only is it a form of relaxation, but you can teach to all of the concepts we have talked about:** planning (what to put in), sensory (they love the feel and smell of soil), sequencing (work the soil first and plant seed second), abstraction (seed turns into a plant, which turns into a vegetable or flower), social interactions (sharing the crop with others). This type of leisure time can easily progress to a career in horticulture or garden design! The biggest plus - plants don't talk back.

- **Regular exercise is recommended** for all of us. For those affected by FASD we need first to evaluate their skills in the areas of balance and hand-eye coordination. Also, we have to clarify whether there are anomalies with muscle mass, bone structure or joint problems to ensure we are not unknowingly causing them harm. Further, many patients have attention problems, so it might be more beneficial to introduce them to sports like running on an outside track as opposed to a treadmill. They won't get bored as quickly, and if they lose their attention, the outdoor track doesn't keep going. (I have my own x-rays to prove it.) My advice to parents is always let them try whatever they seem to gravitate to; kids are pretty instinctive as to what they might be good at. Routine exercise may help with releasing excess energy, alleviating anxiety and improving self-esteem-for both of you! It can be anything from yoga to karate, boxing to gymnastics; again, check with your doctor before starting any fitness regime to make sure it is safe for both of you.

- **Modifications to their physical education program should also be implemented based on their respective physiology.** For example, if they have poor muscle tone and cannot sustain prolonged physical activities, circuit training may not be in their best interest. Discuss with the teacher what alternatives could be worked out, such as enlisting them as the official timekeeper or equipment manager so that they are included and feel they are effectively participating.

- **As discussed earlier, hunger is a feeling, and some children simply don't feel hungry or full depending on their physiological make-up (central nervous system dysfunction).** Some patients may require multiple snacks and nutritional supplements all day as opposed to larger meals. For children that seem to never be full, who will eat five bowls of cereal if you let them, careful nutritional planning is required so that they stay at a healthy weight. It is a fallacy that all affected individuals were a low weight at birth or always skinny later in life. I have some patients that were born the size of a barnyard turkey. Enlist a nutritionist to assist in creating a balanced diet of healthful snacks, because they are likely to be life-long grazers and need to get into good eating habits right from the start.

- **Oral sensitivities or under-sensitivities can cause a great deal of frustration for both children and parents.** You may need to delegate more time for them to finish eating and be patient when it comes to a "splashy" eater. Poor swallowing reflexes, muscle control or problems actually *feeling* the food (being ultra over- or under-sensitive to hot/cold or textures) are usually the culprits. Some patients enjoy brushing their tongue before they eat to desensitize it, and others may have a ritual where they will eat only one food group at a time. They may become uptight if different foods are "touching" because the mixed textures don't feel good once inside their mouth. This is particularly true, for example, where a 13-year-old does not verbally point out that a certain food is not palatable to him; rather, he just opens his mouth and lets it all fall back onto the plate in one big clump. Many kids have trouble coping with food textures - meat, for example - or having several textures in their mouth at the same time like a stew. It would be like us sampling gravel and being expected to finish it. Some parents will puree some foods (like meat) or alter the preparation to make it more pleasing. Others accommodate the menu to foods that their child does enjoy and also prepare a family favourite - all the more for you! Approach eating issues with calmness and understanding and not criticism, because many of their idiosyncrasies were developed due to a physical reason, and not just to be difficult.

- **If your child becomes easily over-stimulated, try small group or one-on-one instructors in everything:** drawing, painting, musical instrument, dance, languages (my friend Emily speaks English, Spanish **and** French), drama, yoga, running, swimming, cooking, rock climbing, sewing or crafts. This doesn't mean that you have to always pay big bucks for private lessons. Check into community programs that have senior volunteers who are interested in mentoring a junior artist, or classes that are specifically for persons of various abilities. If you're feeling that you'd like to get your creative juices flowing, take a class together or try instructional videos!

- As much as possible, **let them work at a large table** instead of a formal desk so they can move around and be more comfortable. Many schools are reverting to "big table teaching" because it appears to be quite effective for children with attention and hyperactivity components.

- **Watch for allergies and reactions to all medications and foods.** For example, some antihistamines can cause irritability and possibly exacerbate negative behaviours. As a parent, trust that if your intuition tells you something is wrong - it is. Make sure to report and discuss any changes in your child, positive or negative, with your family physician for advice.

Comprehension of social rules

- I am frequently asked, **"If a child has a form of brain injury, would you still use consequences?"** In a word -**YES!** Even though your child may not have the configuration of processing abilities to help tell the actual difference between right and wrong, in our society, if one steals, one goes to the slammer as a consequence of that action. To reduce the incidence of the behaviour, make modifications to the environment, such as not leaving money out on the counter if that is your child's profile. In a situation when you catch children red-handed with something that doesn't belong to them, try the two-consequence option. This is where you think up two different consequences and give them a choice. First, identify the inappropriate action: "Billy, this Volkswagen belongs to your sister, Rita. This is called stealing. If you steal, you can go to jail, so you need a consequence. Would you rather have no telephone for two days or no computer for two days?" Because they are given a choice, they still get disciplined, and you have successfully diffused a potential brouhaha. To have some selection in their day, even with a consequence, gives them a feeling of control and boosts self-esteem. Remember, for some patients, we are aiming for rote learning (doing it over and over) where eventually they will just do it regardless whether they actually comprehend why they should. A mom puts it this way: "For my son, not stealing for him is like Valentine's Day for everyone else. We all celebrate it, but we don't know why - we just do it. For him, he knows not to steal because it is simply what we do, but he'll never know why."

- **When explaining consequences, have them design a diagram or list to help visually understand** "if I do this, this will happen." Make a few copies (to account for loss, rips, use as a spit ball, etc.), and have them place it somewhere where they may refer to it easily.

- For older kids, let them come up with what they think would be appropriate, and then **show them the process of arbitration**, on paper, just the way the Teamsters do. This approach gives them a sense of control in decision making and bodes well for them to follow through as they came up with the consequence, and it reduces the chances of a potential hissie-fit. You might be surprised how they respond. Just know that, as with other types of brain dysfunction, the set consequences will work for a while, and then they don't. Rather than be discouraged by this change, see it as an opportunity to never be bored with the same "sentences" over and over again.

- **A lack of inhibition that results in displays of nudity is likely caused by your child's difficulty with impulsivity, attention span and most importantly, their inability to feel embarrassed when they are naked.** For those patients that struggle to remember to arrive clothed when they sit down to the breakfast table or forget to close the bathroom door, visual reminders are advisable. It can be as easy as having children choose or draw a large STOP sign with a visual cue to remind them to be dressed before they leave the bedroom or the toilet (close the door and flush). Getting them into a regular routine of dressing or undressing in a certain room (bathroom or bedroom) and directly after bathing will help.

- **Encourage your child to show people that he or she cares for them by teaching manners and etiquette.** Our society has somehow lost our previous protocols of politeness, civility and decorum. It is time to get back to basics and re-teach children respect and courtesy for others and realize that, to some extent, our kids need to be deprogrammed from television, videos or the rude kid down the street that illustrates the "me first" generation. Many cities have manners classes that have proven to be very effective; better yet, get a group together and run your own class and teach one manner at a time until they master it. Show them how to write a thank-you letter or a drawing for gifts they receive; help them bake some cookies for grandma or a special teacher. It's a great way to model appropriate social behaviour, and they are likely to be well received by the people to whom they extended gratitude or generosity.

- **Make a game of what to do in a certain social situation** and have them come up with multiple choice answers and practice. For example, Question: "You and your friend meet a person that you know but you cannot remember their name. What do you do?" Response: "Ignore them (1 point), pretend not to see them (1 point), run away

(1 point), tell them you are sorry but you have forgotten their name and introduce your friend (10 points).

- **Acknowledge when your child has done something right or fitting in a social situation.** For example, "Thank you for helping me set the table" along with a visual cue (like pointing to the table) and attach an emotional response, ". . . that made me feel good."

- **In dealing with inappropriate behaviours, focus more on the "what would have been a better choice" rather that getting stuck on the "why" of what they did.** If you continue to focus on the "why," it is guaranteed to make you batty and you run the risk of conditioning **yourself** into perseverating behaviour! Ask yourself, do I need to be right or do I want it to work?

- **Encourage personal hygiene** by focusing on routine, organization and repetition, and start this program as soon as they can walk. Have them bathe at the same time everyday as much as possible. Allow them to choose personal hygiene products, and colour code combs, toothbrushes and towels so they are more apt to use these and not someone else's. Set a reasonable time for regular bathing (relaxation baths can be longer), and use a built-in timer or a cooking timer to prompt them when to get out. For bath lovers that need a reminder to turn the water off, give them indelible ink so they can draw a line when the water reaches that level. Also, before the prepubescent stage start them on using daily deodorant and shaving with a safe, electric razor to get them into the hang of it. Invite them to try on different colognes or perfumes and look through hair-do magazines to help identify their idea of looking well groomed. Regular checks for "food jewellery" on clothing are one way of finding some humour in being sloppy. (I know because I'm pretty sure I invented that term.) These early-on strategies give them a sense of independence, and the rote routine will promote good lifelong hygiene habits. *I always suggest putting a heat regulator on the taps to prevent the possibility of accidental scalding, particularly for kids that have a high tolerance for pain and/or attention problems.

- **Reaching puberty can pose challenges for all children, but for those with processing difficulties, it can be slightly more complicated.** It is wise to talk to children early on before they reach their teenage years, and find a book or video that is geared towards your child's learning style and *developmental* age. There are many resources like this found in Special Needs library sections, or ask your local Children with Disabilities group for a list of publications. For girls, it is important to set up a strict routine for personal menstrual hygiene in changing feminine hygiene products regularly in the day and not on a "when needed" basis. It may also be helpful to ask for some assistance from your child's doctor in reaffirming what to expect and to establish a connection for further discussions down the road. Masturbation, sexual contact and birth control should also be addressed, and again, there are resources available. As unpleasant as it may feel, it is important that your child receive accurate information in terms he or she understands, with firm rules established regarding what is acceptable and what is not. By keeping an ongoing line of communication open about these issues, the more likely your child will discuss concerns with you and/or your doctor if they arise.

- **Create situations you know will be successful for them, and you.**

Social emotional presentation

Unfortunately, many affected children have experienced a number of residential placements in their short life course, including extended family, foster homes and perhaps adoptive home disruptions. This series of events, combined with weakened processing skills, will stretch a child's coping abilities and impede emotional/social presentation. For some patients regardless of age group, continual use of the suggested strategies is intended to strengthen their ongoing skill development.

- **Colour is a vibrant and compelling tool.** Try studying and using colours to describe feelings, make comparisons and arouse discussions. I have one patient who can tell people what kind of mood they are in by the "colour" she sees in an aura surrounding them. That is how fine-tuned her visual observation skills are. What a spectacular gift Cheryl has! You can explore the power of colour in a million ways, by fooling around on a computer to find backgrounds in various hues, going to a paint shop and gathering samples, discovering the world of a fabric store, experimenting with oil and water colour paints. We all involve our children in choosing their room colour, but go one further and introduce them into the broader range of the spectrum. Certain hues are soothing and comforting while some incite exhilaration. Find out what they (and you) are drawn to, and incorporate these as part of your everyday lives in clothing, space and cherished personal belongings.

- Parents are often bewildered that although they

have tried very hard to instil confidence and self-esteem into their children, it still seems like an uphill battle. A major aspect to consider is that many individuals instinctively feel different from their peers regardless of their abilities. It is hard to be different, especially when it is so complicated to understand why. As a result, they tend to need constant "boosters" to counteract these feelings of insecurity. Encourage children to develop positive statements reflecting issues to be achieved: "I am happy and always do my best." **Focus on the possibilities and not the negatives.** Optimism can take them a long way in making it a self-fulfilling prophecy.

- **Give them an assignment that you know they can do before introducing a new concept where you anticipate that they may have some trouble.** This boosts their self-confidence, rendering them more eager to start something more challenging. For those that have Verbal processing problems, ask them to show you (demonstrate) what they know as opposed to telling you.

- **Apologize when necessary; as adults we tend not to apologize to children as much as we do with other adults.** In particular for children who have had little stability in life, it is more likely that adults have rarely, if ever, apologized for their own inappropriate behaviour. As mistakes happen, it is helpful to model apologies, if warranted, in order to demonstrate the appropriate response that one would expect. For example, "I'm sorry I yelled at you. Let's try again." Modelling will demonstrate that although an unpleasant incident happened, it can be resolved through initiating a concession. Just as important is commending children when they do apologize, even if you think they are not really sorry (as they likely don't think they did anything wrong). Nonetheless, it is a much-needed skill to get through life, it depicts to others that their feelings were acknowledged, and it reduces defensiveness, leading to improved communication for both parties. If we get stuck on the "He says he's sorry, but I know he isn't," we are unable to shift from the paradigm of "This is part of his brain injury, not wilful disrespect," which will continue to frustrate the both of you, forever.

- **Play charades and include social situations.** Get out the jar and choose a theme like "Dating," and write down potential situations that could come up in dating and act them out. There is nothing grosser to a 13-year-old than watching mom and dad huddled in an imaginary parked car. It can help alleviate any defensiveness in even bringing up such issues, and hopefully it may give you some ideas for later when the kids are all in bed.

- **Bolster their self-esteem by writing "bonus" notes** such as "You're a great son!" and place them somewhere as a surprise, such as in the sock drawer or lunch bag. Send one to yourself or spouse, too.

- **Music can be therapeutic if you choose well.** It is amazing what kids latch on to when they are exposed to a variety of types of music. There are so many wonderful ways to experiment with music, from going to the public library, to going to a music shop and using the headsets, to asking friends to borrow tunes that you might not otherwise ever listen to. A dad talks about his love of music and the connection that it made with his son: "I woke up one morning, and as I came downstairs, Jack had all of my coveted Beatles albums strewn all over the living room floor. I'm sure my heart stopped. My wife and I had just finished talking over our new ways of approaching things with him, so I took a deep breath and stopped myself from screaming. He looked up at me with such excitement and awe and said, "Dad! Wait until you hear these guys - they are so good I can't stop listening to them!" We spent the better part of the day talking and listening to the music. We have learned a lot about each other since that day."

- **Let them know that nobody is perfect and that we all make mistakes.** Give them instances of others, even you, making a boo-boo, and explain how you dealt with it. Honesty is the best policy, and they will learn from your example.

- **Take photographs of your child participating** in a sport, chatting with a friend, doing something where he or she is obviously having a great time. A photographic memory of good experiences, artwork or other achievements can be a nice reminder on a lousy day.

- **Strengthen their abilities to label and link facial emotions.** One clever mom took her child to the store and let her choose a pretty gold hand mirror. When they got home, they practiced looking into it and identifying various feelings. On a day when her daughter came home very upset and starting to escalate, mom pulled the mirror out of the drawer and put it in front of her directing: "Look, Melissa, this is angry; say 'I am angry.'" Over time, this strategy proved effective in Melissa's improving her ability to verbalize how she felt, but she also was better able to read facial emotions of her peers. Brilliant!

- **Guide them into safe, structured friendship that**

allows them to do things without parents or siblings all of the time. Scout out peers that will be a positive influence, and busy them to reduce the chances of befriending an unsavoury character. Don't be afraid to say no. Corruption by associates that engage in negative behaviours will grab your child faster than you can say "jail-house-rock." Surround them with places to meet solid friends in activities like youth groups, short interest courses, church, camps and school clubs; seek out those with supportive parents. See if a family member, Elder, neighbour, older teen or adult volunteering with a reputable agency may be interested in mentoring your child.

- **Caring for animals has many rewards, including giving children someone to talk to that doesn't judge but needs them as much as they need the animal.** Aside from dogs and cats, there are even equine therapy classes springing up for children and adolescents that have been previously mistreated, and these seem to really be working. If your child seems to take to certain animals, talk to the experts on that particular species and get information about it. Have your child tend to the animal, or if a pet doesn't work in your household, see if you could arrange visits with a friend's animal or have your child volunteer at the humane shelter. It might not be for everyone but this method has been tried and true in my practice. Several patients have gone on to having careers with animals as a groom, ranch hands and veterinary assistants! One is also a security man for a rock band, but he says that doesn't count. Love what you do and the luck will come!

- **Let them know they are not all that different from other people and they are certainly not alone.** In perspective, we all learn differently and have quirks and foibles, and there are billions of people that have disabilities of all kinds. Give them concrete examples of other people who have worked within their disability, like movie star Tom Cruise disclosing his dyslexia. Parents of any child who has challenges, physical, cognitive and/or with mental health, will tell you that they achieved success by accentuating their child's abilities and accepting the drawbacks. It is a very fine line to balance between acknowledging to your child that she or he has it harder than some people and not allowing it to become an excuse. Focus on the affirmative, and it will serve you both well.

- **Many of us are creative in some way but just don't know how to tap into it.** Appreciate that many things are an art, not just drawing or painting. If they like to copy a cartoon character - that's art! If their poetry contains a few expletives, see it as artistic expression and rejoice in their creativity; do not just complain about the use of a couple of swear words. If their band's music is similar to the sounds of giving birth, stick in some earplugs and start tapping your foot. They'll never notice that you can't hear, but they will notice that you're proud of their efforts.

- There has been much speculation about the effectiveness of standard cognitive therapy with FASD patients due to many having weak verbal processing skills and not seemingly benefiting from traditional "talk" therapy. Nonetheless, many therapists have educated themselves and have made adjustments to their practice by including the parent's assessment of how their child best learns. Incorporating shorter sessions and including visuals and other creative techniques are now being used to cover areas of concern. **It is a fallacy that affected individuals do not require or benefit from counselling, especially if there has been sexual or physical abuse.** Procuring treatment that is designed to their learning style and neurological sensitivities is the answer, as we know all patients are different. Due to the nature and variability of FASD, alternative therapies such as massage therapy, aromatherapy and equine therapy all have promising therapeutic possibilities for constructive interventions. Again, it is the clinician's knowledge base and acceptance of FASD as a medical disability that are likely to prove most valuable to the patient and family.

- **Keep in mind that much of what you might see in your child is typical stage behaviour.** FASD or no FASD, teenagers can be absolutely awful people for at least a few long months or, God forbid, years, as this behaviour is a customary prerequisite for a sturdy adulthood. Ten-year-old boys break wind at the dinner table and then laugh to tears if you let them - it is almost a right of passage. Finding the balance between what is "normal" and what isn't is not as difficult as you might think. Look back and around to reclaim perspective. You were young once, right?

We are now going to start to create prevention strategies and intervention techniques for your child. **Combine the Strengths List, CNS Checklist and Abilities List.** Using the **Strategy Guide**, choose the approaches that are best suited to your child's specific abilities. You are ready to begin designing strategies using the **OBD 3 Step Plan of Action!**

Chapter Seven

The OBD 3 Step Plan of Action!

The **OBD** 3 Step Plan consists of designing prevention strategies and intervention techniques based on the *overall* executive functioning of the individual; the focus is on identification of strengths and interests, while acknowledging their limitations. Incorporating your parenting or teaching style into this plan is crucial in order to create ideas that work for both you and your child. To be clear, our goal is to reduce the incidence of some behaviour and not expect complete elimination of the behaviour. As a parent or teacher you may be in a position to educate others, particularly "sceptics," regarding the ramifications of FASD. Although it may be tempting to disregard Step 2, don't. By discussing the common societal interpretations of presenting behaviours, the person thinking these will identify with them and likely be more willing to listen. The purpose of Step 2 is not to embarrass anyone; it is there to give people an opportunity to revise their understanding of the root cause of the child's behaviour. A clear explanation, with examples of how cognitive processing problems *translate* to seemingly wilful, defiant behaviours, is the key to cultivating more positive attitudes towards the child, youth or adult. Our objectives are to focus on their strengths while acknowledging their challenges, and to provide as much consistency as possible at home and school and within the community.

Step 1) <u>Behaviour:</u> Sally has **trouble completing homework or a chore.**

Step 2) <u>Possible Societal Misinterpretations of the Behaviour:</u> She's **lazy, oppositional, intentionally defiant, stubborn,** has

unsupportive parents and/or is **irresponsible.**

Step 3) <u>Central Nervous System Dysfunction Issues that *Translates* to behaviour:</u> Sally is diagnosed with **Attention Deficit Disorder** and problems with **distractibility,** and has difficulty processing verbal **communication, sequencing** and **abstract concepts.** Confirmed **short-term memory deficit.**

Now, use the **Strategy Guide** suggestions from the areas that best pertain to your child. For example, if she or he has trouble with **abstract concepts** as above, then choose strategies from the **Abstraction strategies list.** Once you've got the hang of it, design your own creative blueprint based on your child's **Strengths and Abilities Lists** and your style of parenting!

Our Prevention Strategies and Intervention Techniques

- We will ask the teacher to provide a photocopy of the assignment as opposed to having Sally trying to copy it, as she really struggles in that area. At home, we will print out requests for her to follow.

- Make sure to give Sally a visual/verbal cue so she knows where to start. She chose a pink highlighter pen, and we help her to highlight the part that is important to get done first, second and so on.

- Consider the possibility that we put the request in abstract terms that she did not understand. We should say, "Sally, pick up the clothes on the floor and put them in the hamper" instead of "pick up your room."

- Sally is really into horses, so we will use horses when

helping her with her math concepts by showing her pictures of six horses (which we photocopied and she cut out) and multiply them by two, having her figure out the answer. She has to write a story, so she is writing one about a pony. She likes horse stickers, and we will use them for rewards for completing her homework.

- She has a test on Friday, so we are practicing remembering the words in her favourite song: "R-E-S-P-E-C-T find out what it means to me!"

- Sally is very tactile and likes the feel of sand. To help her with abstract concepts and memory we could play a game where we fill a big bowl with sand and bury objects in it, then have her guess what it is. The prize - horse charm!

- She has trouble in the morning when we ask her to dress herself. To remind her where things are she cut out pictures of socks, underwear and t-shirts from old magazines, and we taped them to her drawers where the items are kept. Since she has trouble putting outfits together (it causes us both grief), we are going to try hockey-hangers where we can put an outfit together ahead of time all on one hanger. That way she can just pull them out of the closet and get dressed quickly without frustration.

- This weekend we are going to take photographs of her doing her chores. We will then have her choose on the digital camera which pictures to keep, and have her put them up where she thinks she'll remember to look at them. I am taking shots of her father doing dishes as well - there's always hope.

- We are getting her to try using a Dictaphone to help remind her of things she needs to do.

- Sally likes to help her younger brother, so on Sunday we are going to use visuals with verbal instruction and tactile objects to reinforce learning. He is learning his colours, so she will teach him orange by wearing orange, paint with orange, use orange paper, point out orange objects in the room, have an orange as a snack, and point out that dad's favourite football team is dressed in orange.

The OBD 3 Step Plan of Action!

Step 1) <u>Behaviour:</u> Doug's problem is **lying,** or we might say **"storytelling."**

Step 2) <u>Possible Societal Misinterpretations of the Behaviour:</u> He has been blamed for **deliberate deception,** being **generally dishonest,** having a **lack of conscience,** being **manipulative;** he has been called a **cheater, untrustworthy** and even a **sociopath** at his young age.

Step 3) <u>Central Nervous System Dysfunction Issues that *Translates* to Behaviour:</u> **Memory deficit, sequencing problems,** difficulties with **abstract concepts,** attempting to say what he thinks it is you want him to say because he is great at reading visual cues

Our Prevention Strategies and Intervention Techniques

- Our first clue that he is a very concrete, literal thinker was when I asked him to answer the door and he responded, "but it's not talking." Note to self - he's got a point and made me laugh.

- Our child has weak verbal skills - we need to check out

if he understood the question by rephrasing to be more specific: "Were you at John's house?" instead of "Where were you?"

- Give two choices (as opposed to a general question): "Did you go to John's house or the 7-11 store?"

- If we know he has problems with putting things in the right order (sequencing), let's try having him use visual markers (which is a strength for him) such as the store, school or friend to help him re-enact what happened and try to remember the correct order. In a more serious situation, we may actual take him in the car to see if that helps him piece the events together more accurately.

- Doug has difficulty with abstraction and timeframes. He is embarrassed that he has trouble telling time and gets frustrated; he loses track of time and then panics when explaining himself. We talked about it and we're getting him a cool watch that has a built-in alarm that he can pre-program to remind him when to come home from his friend's house.

- Is there a possibility that he is borrowing someone else's story and making it his own because he can't think of how to answer? Is this because my face and body language are telling him he is in big, big trouble so he's making things up just to be able to give an answer? I'll check myself and change my demeanour to assure him that it is more important to get the story straight.

- If he is saying he forgot to do something we asked him to, are we sure he hasn't simply just forgotten because of his problems with his memory? Did he get distracted somehow? We'll retrace the events and see if we could have reminded him somehow to get the job done.

- When we ask Doug a question we have to be mindful of not using long sentences and then getting angry when he "fills in" the blanks to compensate for what he didn't "hear."

- If we are certain he has lied just to get out of trouble, we have him create a chart that outlines rules and consequences. He makes a visual reminder by drawing a cartoon (one of his talents) with a caption of him telling a true statement and another with the untrue statement with the consequence attached to the untrue statement. He chose no computer games for a day, so he drew a picture of the computer with a red line through it to remind him of the consequence of telling an untruth. We followed through with the consequence, and Doug accepted it as he was part of the process.

- People get very frustrated with Doug because of the "lying." He loves to paint, so we asked him to make our Christmas cards this year, and it really made a difference with his self-esteem as people went out of their way to tell him how great they were!

The OBD 3 Step Plan of Action!

Step 1) <u>Behaviour:</u> George is **often late** or **does not show up**.

Step 2) <u>Possible Societal Misinterpretations of the Behaviour:</u> George is often viewed as **disrespectful, irresponsible.** He has also been labelled **passive/aggressive, inconsiderate, apathetic** and having **disregard for authority figures** (for example, in court cases, where a youth fails to appear).

Step 3) <u>Central Nervous System Dysfunction Issues that _Translates_ to Behaviour:</u> George's test results indicated that he has great difficulty in being able to understand **abstract concepts** (such as time) and problems with **organization.** He is very **distractible,** and on the way to work something or someone else sometimes distracts him. He also has **memory deficits** (forgets where he is going or how to get there) and a weakness in forming cause-and-effect concepts **(problem solving).** For example, he'll be late for work and panic, so he just doesn't go even though he is only a little late. George has **soft neurological signs** (sleep problems and has trouble waking up in the early morning).

Our Prevention Strategies and Intervention Techniques

- George really wants to try using a computerized organizer, so we're going to look for a second-hand one, as he is willing to split the cost.

- Replace his watch with a pre-programmed alarm.

- He requires verbal reminders (telephone call) if no one else is home. Dad will take Monday and Wednesday, Mom will take Tuesday and Thursday, and his sister will take Friday; we split up the work.

- George has a lot of trouble getting up in the morning. We need to encourage him to look for a job that starts later in the day.

- He has been late or not shown up because he has lost his bus pass. We are going to laminate it, and he is going to buy a trendy chain to attach to it on his belt.

- George came up with his own strategy of wearing his headset on the bus and the fourth song is about where he needs to get off!

The OBD 3 Step Plan of Action!

Step 1) <u>Behaviour:</u> Tara has had **trouble setting the table.** For example, she will set it for two people when there are five people in the family.

Step 2) <u>Possible Societal Misinterpretations of the Behaviour:</u> She was seen as **disrespectful, self-centred, immature** (wants mother all to herself), **indolent, lazy** or **rude.**

Step 3) <u>Central Nervous System Dysfunction Issues that *Translates* to Behaviour:</u> She has great difficulty understanding **abstract concepts.** Tara is a very visual, concrete thinker (strength). She also has short- and long-term **memory deficits.**

*In this instance, there were two people in the room (the daughter and the mother) at the time when she was asked to set the table.

Our Prevention Strategies and Intervention Techniques

- We realized later that she used her strengths in visual learning to link the place settings with what was in front of her - her and me. Even though we have five in the family, she cannot see in her mind that there are three other people that need place settings. We have to remember for tasks like this; we need to work with her through the steps: How many people live at our house? Then how many plates do we need?

- We have a lot of activities and Tara really enjoys setting a nice table. We now have a blackboard in the kitchen where everyone checks off what night they will not be home for dinner so she can adjust on a daily basis. We also advise of changes in schedule if company is coming ahead of time, so she writes it down to remind herself.

- Since Tara enjoys the job of setting the table, her sister bought her a Martha Stewart and other decorating magazines. Since then, she has started using things from around the house to make the table more festive!

- Tara has good fine motor skills and is going to try sewing place mats on the machine. We will get her a pattern and work together on the steps, as that is easier for her to follow. She is also very tactile and seems already to enjoy working with different fabrics. Another plus is that she says sewing relaxes her and she is proud of her creations!

- We mentioned Tara's new table design hobby to her teacher and she is going to ask her to do a table setting for the staff luncheon for extra credit.

The OBD 3 Step Plan of Action!

Step 1) Behaviour: **A teenage girl newly placed into foster care is told to make a peanut butter and jam sandwich and is discovered standing in the kitchen licking peanut butter off her hand.**

Step 2) <u>Possible Societal Misinterpretations of the Behaviour:</u> **Laziness,** assumption of previous **neglect, emotional disturbance, attention seeking, immature, "pushing buttons"** to get back at parent, **psychiatric problems.**

Step 3) <u>Central Nervous System Dysfunction Issues that *Translates* to Behaviour:</u> **Sequencing problems** (what is the correct order and sequence in making a peanut butter and jam sandwich), **memory deficit** (even though she may have been shown before, does not have consistent mastery of the task), **abstract thinking** (unable to generalize or see patterns).

Our Prevention Strategies and Intervention Techniques

- Disregard standards based on her chronological age (12) as to what she "should" be doing, and give her supports to help her act and feel as independent as possible.

- We should not assume that she automatically knows the sequence of things that require many steps.

- Ask yourself, how many steps are there in making a sandwich? About 48 (go to the pantry, get the peanut butter, put it on the counter, open the fridge, get the jam, etc., etc.). Make sure that we are not assuming that something is simple when it isn't.

- Use visual cues to teach sequences. A picture plan is a visual reminder of what you want her to do, with a numbered sequence of directions.

- Make a "recipe" list and have her cross off each direction when it is completed.

- Practice other methods of improving sequencing, such as coloured beadwork that she wants to learn with her grandmother.

The OBD 3 Step Plan of Action!

Step 1) Behaviour: **During story time Joey repeatedly moves himself to the back of the class, even when told not to by the teacher; he receives a daily consequence for the inappropriate behaviour.**

Step 2) Possible Societal Misinterpretations of the Behaviour: He is **attention seeking,** has a **disregard** for **authority figures,** is **manipulative** or **intentionally disruptive.**

Step 3) Central Nervous System Dysfunction Issues that *Translates* to Behaviour: **Memory, abstract concepts** (time), **ADHD** (finds it hard to sit still), **easily over-stimulated.**

*After examining what was happening before, during, and after story time, we realized that Joey had story time every day and then the school bell rang. The problem was that on different days the next class changed - one day it was gym and another day was art class. In this instance, he created his own strategy by spending story time moving behind the other students so he could follow them (strong visual skills) and know where to go next.

- Now he gets a verbal/visual from the teacher: "We are now going to the gym," and she points in the gymnasium's direction. The teacher's aide (or student buddy) will tell him which activity will happen next (so he doesn't worry) and forewarn him one minute before it is over to remind him where he will be going next.

- He made a schedule in colours so he knows that red is gym and yellow is art class.

- As Joey finds transitions or changes in routines quite stressful, he is told ahead of time about school concerts, assemblies, field trips or fire drills.

*If children are extremely hyperactive (ADHD), think about whether it may be in everybody's best interest to not insist that they attend the family wedding, reunion or shopping on a Saturday on 70% off day. If you know they can't cope with crowds due to over-stimulation sensitivities, offer something else that they would like to do rather than set it up as a punishment. Give them something to look forward to if they can't go. Alternatively, break the length of stay down to accommodate what they can handle. Make clear to family and friends that you and your child need their support. Explain that his or her absence it is not a slight towards them or that you are spoiling your child. Let them know that accommodating to special needs is no different from putting up a ramp for someone who requires a wheelchair.

The OBD 3 Step Plan of Action!

Step 1) <u>Behaviour:</u> **Ripping nightgown, refusing to wear socks.**

Step 2) <u>Possible Societal Misinterpretations of the Behaviour:</u> The child has **Oppositional Defiant Disorder,** is **stubborn, destructive, spoiled,** or **possibly previously sexually abused.**

Step 3) <u>Central Nervous System Dysfunction Issues that *Translates* to Behaviour:</u> **Soft neurological signs** (extreme sensitivity to touch, tactile defensiveness).

Our Prevention Strategies and Intervention Techniques

- Monitor ill fitted clothing and elastic wristbands on nightwear.

- Remove all tags from the back of the neck or anywhere inside clothing. We found one on the side of her nightshirt as well as on the back.

- Wash clothes repeatedly, prior to wear if necessary; or stock up on previously worn clothing.

- Purchase cotton clothing as much as possible (it breathes). Many other fabrics can cause extreme discomfort, so take them along to shop for new things.

- Turn socks inside out: it might be the seam on the toe that is aggravating them, or the socks may be too tight around the ankles.

The OBD 3 Step Plan of Action!

Step 1) <u>Behaviour:</u> Lee-Jay is a **collector of other people's things** (or stealing).

Step 2) <u>Possible Societal Misinterpretations of the Behaviour:</u> He has been branded as being **intentional dishonest,** having **no conscience;** we have been accused of **inadequate parenting;** he has been referred to as **sneaky, greedy** and having a **lack of remorse.**

Step 3) <u>Central Nervous System Dysfunction Issues that _Translates_ to Behaviour:</u> Lee-Jay presents with extreme **impulsivity;** he is unable to draw cause and effect based on past experiences **(problem solving),** visual perceptual difficulty (space) **(soft neurological sign),** unable to process **abstraction,** and **memory deficit,** and he does not **comprehend social rules.**

Our Prevention Strategies and Intervention Techniques

- We keep photographs of everyone that lives in the house handy. If we find him with an item that is not his (and the owner is not home), we _physically pair the item with the picture of the person_ to provide a visual cue of ownership. This makes an abstract concept (the absent owner) concrete. We explain: "If we take it without asking, it is called stealing," and reiterate that if we steal, we go to jail. Then we give him a choice of two consequences from a potential consequence list we made with him. As parents, we have agreed to consistently deliver the consequences. We are not expecting that he will eventually _comprehend_ why, but through rote learning we hope to establish that stealing is something we don't do. *If the owner were available, we would use him or her for this lesson instead of the picture.

- We use masking tape to define each half of the boys' shared bedroom.

- We also had him make a big Keep Out sign, and he put it on his sister's door to provide him with a visual reminder of her space and boundaries.

- We are going to take him shopping to choose one colour for his personal items like toothbrush, towel, comb and gel so his sister doesn't kill him.

- I put my heirloom figurines in my bathroom, since he gave away one and broke two. Now, he and I don't have to worry because he never goes in there. It turns out I enjoy them even more now that I can see them when I'm relaxing in the tub!

- We devised a chart together that outlines the rules and consequences for everyone. It is a visual reminder that is posted in the kitchen at his eye level.

The OBD 3 Step Plan of Action!

Step 1) Behaviour: **A child does not cry when being taken from his parents by a social worker to a foster placement; rather, he is excited and leaves eagerly.**

Step 2) Possible Societal Misinterpretations of the Behaviour: He **doesn't love me (us), doesn't care,** is **egocentric,** is **deliberately making us feel bad** for rejecting him, he is **ungrateful** or **happy about moving** to another home.

Step 3) Central Nervous System Dysfunction Issues that _Translates_ to Behaviour: He is powerless to process **abstract concepts,** doesn't know where he is going, for what length of time, and doesn't understand the ramifications for his future **(problem solving).** He thinks in the here and now. He has language deficits **(communication skills),** so he is unable to verbalize his feelings or attach words to his emotions. Additionally, he has perceptual deficits, so he cannot accurately interpret other people's emotions; due to his type of CNS dysfunction, he has no sense of "stranger danger," so he goes willingly **(social/emotional presentation).**

Our Prevention Strategies and Intervention Techniques

- We made an error in assuming that he knows how to label feelings just because he is a big kid and "should" know how to do that by now. We realize that we need to re-evaluate our expectations in that area.

- We may need to teach him by using photographs and drawings (visuals) that depict different emotions. For example: "This is what sad looks like," and then discuss what to do when we see someone is sad such as "I will ask if they are ok and if I can help."

- We're going to try out sign language signals (codes) to see if that helps him tell us what is going on for him. We are also arranging to talk to a speech therapist to get techniques that may be helpful.

- We are going to try other methods of communicating like experimenting with games and note writing.

- He is good at writing, so to open the lines of communication, we will ask him if it is easier sometimes to write down what is hard for him to say. His learning style tells us that it is easier for him to understand when the information is visual (he struggles with verbal instructions or conversation). When he writes us to communicate, we are going to answer him by writing back. We will print and not use longhand as he finds print easier to read.

*Evaluate whether your child is a very concrete thinker and learns by seeing things. If so, it is likely that he or she will mimic hitting if exposed to it. If you spank, chances are at some point, you will see this behaviour repeated in some form at any age. For children that have been exposed to physical abuse, regardless of their age, modeling appropriate ways to deal with anger and confusion is critical. This will take extreme patience as they may be deeply hurt and afraid, and have not been taught alternatives for dealing with their feelings. Watch for signs of upset such as increased aggression, depression and/or sleep disruptions. These may be signals of the only way they know how to express their emotions. If this is compounded by weaker verbal skills, give them other options based on their strengths to deal with their pain: like drawing, boxing, poetry, or if they have strength in writing, have them write a letter to whom ever they are mad at - even you. Assess for yourselves whether it might be helpful to enlist professional assistance for guidance in this area; make sure that they have expertise and training in dealing with kids of this disability.

The OBD 3 Step Plan of Action!

*This example was designed to give to the residential staff that will soon be working with Stephen. He is 20 years old and soon moving into a supported living situation. The parents suggested to the staff that they might want to use the OBD 3 Step Plan of Action! in their weekly staff meetings. This way, the staff members can learn together, and support both Stephen and each other appropriately.

Step 1) <u>Behaviour:</u> He can become **aggressive** and have **tantrums.**

Step 2) <u>Possible Societal Misinterpretations of the Behaviour:</u> He is a **bully, mean, overtly defiant of authority, oppositional,** has a **lack of remorse, wilfully intends to harm,** is **spoiled.**

Step 3) <u>Central Nervous System Dysfunction Issues that *Translates* to behaviour:</u> Steven's biggest challenge is **impulsivity,** and he becomes very easily **over-stimulated** due to the problem he has processing verbal directions or conversation **(communication skills).** He struggles to formulate cause-and-effect thinking based on past experience ("If I do this, that will happen . . ."). Steven has a slow processing speed leading to confusion, **soft neurological signs** (and high sensitivity to environment). He can <u>present</u> as quite immature **(social/emotional issues)** as his developmental functioning is considerably lower than chronological age.

Our Prevention Strategies and Intervention Techniques

- Consider fight, flight or fright may be his way of letting you know that he is overwhelmed and doesn't understand, but has great difficultly expressing it verbally. Check out whether there were too many directions or words put together in a run-on sentence that might have confused him. A system can be developed of giving him an option of a "code" where he has a private agreement with staff that when he has become upset, he places a small brightly coloured Post-It note on the table, which is a signal that he requires clarification.

- Check to make sure you are not using sarcasm or innuendo, for example, to be funny. He has great difficulty determining what it means, and it may trigger him to become defensive. He reads your face and listens to the tone of your voice to try to help him understand what you are saying.

- Try to estimate how much frustration is in his entire day, and identify the "hot spots." Work with him towards reducing the incidence in some areas by giving him options and adding relaxation techniques *prior* to high stress times. He really enjoys his quiet time where he pulls his comforter completely over his head to black out the light. This routine is helpful for him.

- Realize that although he is twenty years of age, he sometimes responds with behaviour more geared to a nine-year-old level in developmental functioning. Use this as an indicator of where to start by trying behaviour techniques adapted from those for a younger child, but disguise them as "age appropriate" methods so he doesn't feel as if he is being "treated like a baby."

- Focus on empowering him, not controlling him.

- Adjust supervision for high-risk times, like class breaks and lunch hour, by having him do jobs for the school for extra credit. This can be arranged through the counsellor at the college.

- Restrict violent movies, music videos, games (computer and others), television, magazines, friends, books, posters and language. **No exceptions.**

- Because of his sensory sensitivities, we allow the use of headsets, sunglasses or ball caps to assist him in filtering environmental stimuli like bright lighting. (We will pay to install dimmer switches in his room and bathroom.) Certain smells can be very powerful and annoying to him when he is trying to focus, especially certain kinds of incense. He seems to do better on homework while listening to music with a headset as he says it blocks out other distractions. (Sometimes he needs to gyrate his pencil or tap his foot like machine gun fire! Please be respectful of this as it is what works for him and his brain, not ours.)

- Check out all physical factors that might be aggravating him such as hunger, blood sugar, health problems (he is prone to ear and bladder infections), visual impairment (does he have his glasses?), inappropriate clothing (did he remove the tags on new clothing?), or fatigue. He gets a bit crabby at about four p.m. if he is tired or hungry and usually is both. People don't grow out of FASD, so these issues are often overlooked the older the individual is.

- When he is required to complete a task that he may not want to do, give him a choice: for example, "Would you like to do it here or in the bedroom?" If this doesn't work and it *absolutely* has to be done, please follow through with a consequence.

- Consistently issue a consequence for inappropriate behaviour and be sure to describe it visually and verbally in conjunction with a pre-determined consequence, or a choice of two consequences. The language has to be consistent for him, so use familiar words: angry, frustrated and bugging me (his contribution). In situations where he is becoming out of control, gently encourage him to calm down *completely* before discussing the consequence; this will reduce the chance of further escalation. It is very important that you attempt to remove yourself from his view if necessary, as *you* become infuriating stimulation, and return only once he is done. Reassure him that you understand that he is upset, and leave him alone for a while. Acknowledge that you recognize you may be aggravating him further at that point. Most people need to feel as if they are heard at this point, regardless of how irrational the issue may be. In a calm moment, it is helpful to discuss how you both could have handled the situation better. By sharing with him that we all make mistakes, he is more apt to listen.

- Encourage him to see movies that depict a person his age in a problem-solving dilemma similar to a situation that relates to his life. It is an excellent way to discuss different ways of dealing with anger and frustration, hurt and pain. (Even when he can be the biggest sourpuss, he enjoys this method, as he doesn't feel singled out. When it's not you directly telling him what to do, it will likely hold his attention longer, and he can watch it as many times as he wants to remind himself.)

- Please identify for him when he managed a potentially upsetting situation and congratulate him knowing how difficult it was for him. (At first when we tried this he ignored us, but he seems to have become more proud of his accomplishments now.)

- Stephen loves soccer (which is a strength and interest for him), so we bought warning cards just like in the game. When he is getting unruly, he gets a yellow warning card. If he continues, he gets a red card, which indicates that he is "out of the game" and has to go to his room. What we didn't count on was that he would use them on us when we were getting on his nerves (lecturing or yelling). It has been a very effective method to keep us all in check!

Chapter Eight

Educating other professionals

Violence and sex on prime time television, kids using obscene language in public places, underwear-exposed fashions, not giving up a seat on the bus to an elderly person, road rage. The world is definitely not the same anymore, and parenting today in general is more complicated and demanding than even a generation ago. Even if you try to instil your personal choice of good manners in your child, others often usurp your authority and, unfortunately, do so in front of your children. How many times have you introduced your child to an acquaintance as Ms. So and So, who has corrected you by saying, "Call me Pat?" For all families perhaps it is time to muster up our courage and let people know the importance of modeling appropriate behaviour and its ramifications for our children. Eons ago, a very brave parent taught me this lesson on my first visit to her home after her five-year-old daughter greeted me with open arms wanting a hug. Without thinking I obliged her, and her mother softly informed me: "I know that she is very cute and cuddly, but we are trying to teach her the difference between a friend and a stranger and you are a stranger." It made a huge impression on me; now I tell this story to everyone I can get my hands on, so that we all have the opportunity to be respectful of parents' decisions for their children, and know that there are valid reasons behind them.

In order to circumvent impending dilemmas you may want to try preparing a **Medical Fact Sheet** documenting pertinent information regarding your child's abilities. Choose with whom it is most appropriate to be shared, such as the current teacher, therapist, social worker, doctor, and respite caregiver or residential placement staff. Be sure to request that the professionals keep the diagnosis confidential; impress upon them that this diagnosis is extremely sensitive because it involves a social issue which identifies two people, your child and his or her biological mother. If you are the biological mother, and if you are ready, let them know - and compliment yourself on your recovery and courage. Most people will understand and respect that you are there to help your child and want the best for him or her to succeed.

Using the basic format, update the **Medical Fact Sheet** over time as your child matures. Consider attaching a sample of the **OBD** Three Step Plan of Action! That way, the person reading it has an opportunity to amend any predisposed or inaccurate notions. As parents, you will have to decide if you are comfortable stipulating the alcohol-related part of the diagnosis or not and whether you feel it will be beneficial. The Medical Fact Sheet should give a brief description of the following areas:

- Physical issues

- Medications

- Ability in conversation skills

- Comprehension or understanding of information

- Day-to-day self-management skills in planning, organizing, anticipating and managing themselves

- Skills in handling money

- Concept of time

- Reading and writing abilities

- Emotional and social maturity and peer relationships

- Supervision requirements

- Interests and hobbies

Here is an example of one for a girl entering junior high school:

Medical Fact Sheet for Mandy

*Please note that the following information is sensitive and confidential and your discretion is very much appreciated. It is intended to provide you with a brief overview of our daughter's abilities and intricacies that are a direct result of her medical disposition.

Medical diagnosis: Static Encephalopathy (brain injury that is not progressive)

Secondary Diagnosis: Attention Deficit Disorder

Medications: Ritalin (given in the morning at home)

Chronological Age: 13 years

Physical issues: Mandy has low endurance for sustained activities due to "soft" muscles, so long distance running or related activities do require some modifications. She is very flexible and has excelled in short-routine gymnastics. Mandy is quite small and thin for her age as a result of her medical condition, which also causes her to have a lack of appetite. She requires medication (Ritalin) for her ADD, which also suppresses what little appetite she has. Mandy has snacks and supplemental drinks in her backpack, and she eats them between class changes. She is also very sensitive to loud, unexpected noises and can become upset quickly, particularly in a fire drill. Last year's teacher found it helpful to have Mandy stay closely beside her and walk out together during the actual drill; she then repeated the action after class in a calmer situation when there was not as much stimulation. This strategy was very effective in teaching Mandy what to do in case of this particular emergency. Mandy finds it difficult to cope with varied bedtimes. She goes to bed at 8:30 p.m. year round, so it is much easier for her to wind down at night and get up in the morning.

Cognitive abilities: Mandy's last Psycho-Educational Assessment (please see copy attached) indicates that, although she is in the overall Average range of intelligence scores, she has difficulty following verbal directions without a visual cue such as pointing, or giving an actual demonstration of what you would like her to do. She needs some assistance in breaking instructions down into steps. Her previous teacher found it helpful to have her write each step on a Post-it note and then cross it off once she completed the task. Please appreciate that her excellent conversational skills do not always equate with her actual comprehension of what you have said to her, especially if the information is put to her in long sentences. When in doubt of whether she understood or not, ask her to put it in her own words. If she cannot respond, we re-word the sentence. Please see her previous Individual Program Plan for details of more strategies.

Mandy has great difficulty in social situations. In developmental age equivalencies her interpretation of peer relationships is developmentally equivalent to that of approximately a ten-year-old child. She requires quite a bit of support in this area because she sometimes becomes upset if she feels ostracized by other teens. We encourage her to write such incidents in her daily diary so that we can discuss the situation after school. We often use role-playing to explain the situation more clearly, and rehearse what she should to do if the situation arises again. Mandy has been assigned to school counsellor Ms. Dunphy; Mandy is aware that she is to go to Ms. Dunphy's office in the event that she is having difficulty with peers or academics. Ms. Dunphy has graciously agreed to stay in regular contact with us and monitor her progress.

Supervision support: Mandy is very easily led by peers and, unlike other teenagers her age, is not able to discriminate inappropriate behaviours. She is enrolled in structured activities each lunch hour with the exception of Fridays, when she is to board the school bus immediately at noon. We would appreciate that we be contacted in the event it appears that she is having any difficulty in this area.

Interests and hobbies: Mandy is an excellent gymnast, practices to relax and enjoys competing. She very much likes to talk about her dog Red. Mandy enjoys doodling, going to the movies, and spending time with her friend Midgy, and she seems to be developing a keen interest in boys.

Thank you for your time and interest in our girl.

*It is recommended that you re-evaluate and update these areas every year in order to verify where children are continuing to blossom, as well as where they might have reached their maximum potential in certain skills. This way you and those involved with your child have the foresight to gradually make the necessary adjustments to school programs, recreational activities, and supervision needs as indicated by progress and not guesswork!

Chapter Nine

Finding perspective

I know you're doing a great job - why don't you?

My best-kept secret in being a home visitor is that even though parents have invited me in to provide suggestions and strategies, guess what? - they already know what they're doing. Usually, they just need someone to reassure them that they're doing the right thing. If you get only one thing out of this entire book, let it be this: **YOU ARE THE EXPERT IN YOUR CHILD!** Other professionals can give you some well-needed insight into their branch of specialization to help you tweak certain areas, but you know your child better than anyone else, regardless of whether you are a birth, foster, adoptive or kinship parent, it doesn't matter. You live with your child 24 hours a day and know his or her idiosyncrasies, habits, tendencies and capabilities. It is with you that your child shares wants and needs, dreams and aspirations. Don't let a 52-professionals-in-attendance meeting rattle your confidence. They should be relying on you for the initial assessment of your child and then contribute ideas to complement what you already know. If they don't seem to believe that this is the way to go, lend them a copy of this book, or fire them and find someone else.

Why are you so hard on yourself and periodically questioning your abilities as a parent? Well, let's see. Since the onset of the diagnosis of FASD you have probably been bombarded with opinions not only from medical doctors (including paediatricians, geneticists, orthodontists, ophthalmologists and various other specialists) but from psychologists, speech/language pathologists, occupational therapists, physiotherapists, social workers, psychiatrists, teachers, principals, special education consultants, in-home support workers, youth workers, counsellors, and your dad who thinks he knows everything (that you're doing wrong) and that all your kid needs "is a good licking." Swell. Ask yourself whether this may have played some havoc with your confidence as a parent. In millennium terminology, ja'think? When parents receive a diagnosis of any medical abnormality in their child, they naturally feel dependant on others to provide information and guide them in what to do next. The biggest problem with this diagnosis is that, although FASD persons have many similarities, the range of disability is so vast that certainties for their future are really difficult to pin down; then again, so is it for all kids. Uncertainty is tough to deal with for *anything* in life, so hang on, look up, hunker down, hope for the best and be kind to yourself and others. You are doing a great job. Believe it.

Attachment

Some parents have disclosed that they sensed something was wrong from shortly after the child's birth. The baby may have not slept much or had to be woken up to feed. Some affected infants are extremely irritable and may have a high-pitched cry (a shrill-like noise comparable to what's heard in bathing suit try-on season). They may have been so sensitive to touch that they could not tolerate being cuddled, or they coo and look into your eyes because it was too bright or over-stimulating for them. It is sometimes next to impossible to soothe and calm them down, and this ordeal could last for months. They are often quite sick babies with bouts of diarrhea, projectile vomiting, and fevers that can be very difficult to console.

Such complications may result in a mother feeling overwhelmed, tired, perhaps unknowingly angry and resentful, further impacting the bonding experience. This is reflected in one mother's comment: "He didn't like to be held, and I felt that he didn't want me." It is difficult for any caregiver to voice such feelings, and many are reluctant to request respite to get some rest from what others see as a little, tiny, harmless baby. Therefore others remain blissfully unaware that this baby can shatter glass with the frequency of her scream, and that her projectile vomiting record stands at ten and a half feet. The fear that we will be scrutinized as an incapable mother or father prevents many of us from taking a well-needed break; unfortunately, a well-intentioned friend, doctor, or relative might reinforce this by saying, "Babies are supposed to cry - you'll get the hang of it." All these factors in combination could not only cause nervous tension, but in the early stages of childhood development may disrupt the bonding experience for the child, parents and siblings. They certainly exacerbate the strains of the physiological factors resultant of prenatal alcohol and/or drug exposure.

A major influence on attachment is instinct. The first human instincts of major importance are the instincts to survive, to be social, and to be adaptable to the environment. How these three instincts interact together is as important as how each functions independently. The significant factors of attachment theory are the physical, emotional and social experiences in early childhood. For children with central nervous system damage, where their feelings of pain, touch, and ability to comprehend or interpret social cues and boundaries have been compromised, it is little wonder that Attachment Disorder would become a common secondary diagnosis. For children that have experienced multiple placements in the care of Social Services this is especially relevant. In addition, raising a child who has experienced previous maltreatment poses potential complications over and above the patient's brain dysfunction. Most children will imitate behaviours that they have been exposed to by the adults in their life. Deciphering which behaviours result from abuse and which are due to the child's neurological problems (interpreting and communicating feelings) can be confusing at best. In either case, the behaviour is likely not an *intentional* effort by the child, rather, a symptom.

To be clear, FASD and Attachment Disorder are *two separate issues* and are mutually exclusive. Some children have a diagnosis of FASD only, and some affected individuals have a secondary diagnosis of Attachment Disorder. The main difficulty is that many behaviours demonstrated in this patient population are similar to the behaviours seen in children diagnosed with Attachment Disorder. For those with a FASD diagnosis the issue becomes what is the appropriate treatment of the disorder? It is imperative that for "combination" kids, the therapeutic intervention should entail a Clinical Therapist (Psychologist, Social Worker, Psychiatrist) who is trained in organic brain injuries and sensitive to the FASD components. Factors of consideration for the clinician would be evaluating (with the assistance of the caregivers) the overall cognitive abilities, executive functioning and variable processing inconsistencies. Sensory sensitivities such as touch and oral stimulation must be considered in "holding therapy," as it sometimes involves blanket wrapping, rocking and bottle feeding with the intention to have the child experience the nurturing that was not available as an infant. This is not a bad idea unless you have a child with extreme tactile defensiveness who is more likely to react by giving you a tactile clue (in the form of a solid slap) of his heightened sensitivity; that would be our fault, not his. Additionally, some patients may not be able to discriminate between pretending to be held as an infant and daily reality; consequently, they may inappropriately mimic this exercise elsewhere. Each case requires careful forethought of these factors in order to design a treatment plan that recognizes the essence of the patient's learning style and physiology, as well as the ramifications for family members.

As difficult as it is, please don't take it personally. It's not that your child doesn't love you; it is that she or he was born with a type of brain dysfunction which has stifled the ability to communicate by physically showing you or by using the right words. We assume that kids are able to label their feelings, but when faced with a "wiring" problem they unconditionally need to be taught how. Since some individuals are disconnected from their own feelings and have difficulty expressing what we would consider the befitting emotion for the circumstance, can we improve on this? The answer is **YES** and you can do it by instilling a daily in-home "therapy" by giving them opportunities to see and label emotions. Change can take years and is most successful when coupled with constant visuals attached to as many distinctive emotional states as possible. Forget about innuendo; many of us don't catch it most of the time anyway, and it can really create confusion for your child. Make new traditions. We can't heal the brain, but by constant repetition, role modeling, and identification with rewards for appropriate emotional responses, we can assist in guiding interpretations of a profoundly emotional world.

In the mean time, have you considered whether **you** are developing a type of attachment disorder of your own? Are you disappointed that your child doesn't seem to love you or your family the way you thought he or she would? Are you detaching physically, emotionally or socially? Are you worried that sometimes you feel that you don't like your child? If you can relate to this (a gentle reminder), these are three important factors of attachment theory that we spoke about earlier; it might be helpful to admit to these feelings and talk to a trusted support person. Getting it out in the open will be a tremendous advantage in making a positive transformation by dealing with your true emotions. Remember, you need to honestly acknowledge the issues in order to effect a constructive change.

Letter therapy . . . writing a mental note to yourself

I suggest letter therapy to parents and young adults that need to "write it out loud!" It works because *you* dictate how personal you want to be, how in-depth you want to go, and what to do with it when it's all done. You have the option to put it away and review it later, burn it, mail it to yourself, or share it with someone else. The choices are all yours and the process can be very powerful, so keep the tissue handy. It is hard to admit that now and then children can really get on your nerves. Sometimes they hurt your feelings, and although you are the adult, it still stings a lot. Ask yourself some questions: Have you been self-medicating with alcohol or prescription medication to cope with stress? Have you considered that you or your spouse may be depressed? Is it possible that you are suppressing resentment towards your child, partner, other children, friends or family? Do you feel guilty, and if so, why? Think about these possibilities and consider what kind of impact they have on you and your family.

The next step in admitting your feelings is to forgive yourself for whatever you think you've done. Forgive yourself for periodically wishing that maybe you shouldn't have adopted or shouldn't have given birth if that's the way you felt. Forgive yourself that you have in some way mistreated your child. Forgive yourself and them for the stress in your marriage and family, and realize that writing it out loud is the first step in re-discovering strength and optimism. Be honest with yourself. It's ok to privately say it out loud. It can be quite liberating. Reminisce about how you were raised, and compare whether that might be a factor in how frustrated you are, because you were taught to parent one way and now it is not working for you or your family. Are you frustrated because you had sworn that you would never talk to your kids the way you were spoken to but have heard yourself sounding much the same way? Forgive their birth mother if it is not you. If it is you, then stop beating yourself up *today*. Once and for all, absolve yourself and the others that brought you to that place in your life. No mom drinks in her pregnancy on purpose; we know that now and so should you. Write down who or what you are mad at and why. Get it all out. The truth really does set you free.

Once you've flushed out the toxins (and pent up feelings *are* pollutants to the mind and body), have a good sleep. The next day, look at it again and make a plan. Make two columns and list the positive things in your life in one and negative in the other. Determine what is going to make it better, and decide what needs to be accentuated or eliminated. Put yourself first for once; really recognize what you need to make this work and feel good about it. Find the balance you need and find the right kind of support. Guaranteed, it will be the start of a new healthy beginning for you and your entire family.

Freeing yourself from toxic relationships

As vocalized repeatedly by caregivers, there may be some people that are involved in our lives in one way or another who are unintentionally harmful to us emotionally and, in some cases, physically. This might be a family member who spanks your child even though you don't use corporal punishment. A friend who is kind enough to baby-sit but continues to let your child stay up two hours past regular bedtime after you have tirelessly explained how detrimental this is for both of you. It could be a well-meaning therapist or doctor who is unaware of the true challenges of parenting an alcohol-affected child, youth or adult and may suggest approaches not suitable for your family. Stand up for yourself and get rid of them. As difficult as this may be, you'll be better off in the long haul.

Another type of problem that can occur is the loss of personal supports. A friend of mine is a single parent of a child with a very debilitating form of brain dysfunction. When her daughter was a baby, and initially diagnosed with her disease, family, friends and colleagues were at the ready with offers to sit with her at the hospital, make meals, run errands and provide moral support to a terrified and exhausted mother. As time went on, the daughter had multiple medical crises, and again everyone rushed to sit vigil with the mother. They patiently listened to her express a multitude of feelings from denial, to rage, to helplessness. The last time my friend called to let me know our girl was in hospital for at least the 27th time, I noticed when I arrived that no one else was there. She was alone to deal with the anguish of having her child scream in pain from insertion of needles for blood-work. By herself at home, she would have to try to hold down her now much bigger and heavier child in order to bag her for a urine sample. She was alone because some people just got tired of listening to the same issues and frustrations. This happened even though her child has a very *observable* form of brain injury, unlike FASD children who are not always visibly disabled. Nonetheless, many of her behaviours are similar to those of some alcohol-affected children.

Take heed and surround yourself with people who are able and willing to hang in there, and fire the one's that cannot. I know one woman who, after years of trying, boldly took a relative aside and said, "I'm firing you as my aunt," and did. If your friends are dwindling, let them know how you feel and either give them a break for a while or find new ones. I once spoke with a lovely lady who was completely distraught because another woman in their support group was causing her more stress than she started out with. Although she was terrified to quit, for fear she wouldn't have support, she realized that it was the best thing she ever did. It was the initial step in focusing on herself and her own needs, and ultimately she gained personal strength. Another stately and very well-mannered lady shared with me that she took herself by total surprise when she told their family psychiatrist to, well, "F" off!" "For years he had me convinced that it was our fault somehow as parents and that her behaviour was in retaliation because she was adopted. We now understand that it is her medical disability and subsequent brain dysfunction that is the root of the problems - not her and not us. Since I stood up to the previous "theories," we have come a long way as a family."

To play it safe, it may also be constructive to examine whether there is a possibility that your child's behaviour has become a source of toxic relationship for both of you. A sensitive issue to ponder for parents is "Have I become toxic in my own home, and/or is my child's behaviour harmful to the rest of the family?" If so, how do we free others and ourselves from this dilemma? Again, it is important to realize that it is the behaviour **caused by FASD,** not the child, which is at the core of these feelings, as they can incite complete dysfunction in otherwise "normal" families. These are parents who never believed in corporal punishment but have surprised themselves by actually hitting their child due to the constant frustration of nothing working to eradicate negative behaviours. In extreme cases, you may have become physically drained or have your health compromised due to a toxic relationship. It can also take the form of physical abuse towards you by your child, or your becoming abusive towards them. If this is your situation, it is time to take immediate action in securing some outside help for your family. Again, the first step is in acknowledging that a situation is out of control; there is certainly more courage in caring about what **you** think and not what everyone else thinks. Do what is best for you and your family.

In some situations, it may be in everyone's best interest to have some form of separation; for some families it may even be permanent. This delicate decision needs to be made with honest deliberation and understanding that it is in everyone's best interest, especially when the dysfunction has led to physical violence. Parents, particularly adoptive and foster parents, may put immense pressure on themselves that a child or youth has to fit in. In some cases they are simply not compatible personalities, and it may be more productive to live separately but maintain familial connections and relationships. For some families this decision has been a life-altering experience because both the youth and family members are more relaxed residing in separate residences. It can evolve into a vast improvement in their relationships. Some families in crisis have found solace in boarding schools and have highly recommended them to other parents. Still other parents who have placed their child into the care of Social Services agencies have given mixed reviews. They caution that there is still a lack of training for and recognition of the specialized needs of an FASD individual, and this situation has resulted in parents' exclusion from decision making regarding even day-to-day activities concerning their child. Sadly, many kids placed in the system end up on the street at some point, which is a harsh reality. Then again, some have flourished in another foster family just because the parents are different, not better. Most importantly, if you are faced with such a decision, start fact-finding. Be truthful and access a non-judgmental support person to accompany you in your decision.

Relinquishing control

One of the hardest issues to deal with in living with persons of brain dysfunction is that affected individuals have very little control in their life. In turn, parents experience a feeling of dwindling control that they wield as parents. Current prime-time talk shows chiefly focus on identifying variations of control issues in relationships such as weight problems, spousal inequality, parent-child conflicts, addictions, disputes over money, sibling rivalry, adult children that won't move out. All these issues of the day have an underlying theme: It is all about control - who has it, and who doesn't. We encourage families of affected children to provide increased supervision that may not correlate with the patient's chronological age, and to carefully structure their time with rigorous routines. Basically, we insist that parents and caregivers be "bossy" in order to sustain equilibrium for their child (fortunately that's not a stretch in our house). The contradiction here is that, in the same breath, we suggest you need to relinquish control of things that are most against the grain, like your child's behaviour. You may feel humiliated when your kid wallops another and then not only doesn't take responsibility but blames everyone else, and flips you off in front of the principal and another parent for good measure. A child's acting inappropriately in our society is considered a direct reflection of parenting skills; with this disability you have to leap over that hurdle. FASD affected persons are not disabled by choice and are not exhibiting behaviours with wilful intent or premeditation. **Be confident that you are doing the best job possible in these contradictory circumstances; you need to believe that when you run into others who are not as aware:** "It really helped me to know that he simply can't help the way his brain works and that the way he acts is because of it. Now that I really understand that I don't get as frustrated anymore and have more patience. That is what has helped both of us the most."

So how do you relinquish control? Many parents have borrowed tried and true methods from established self-help programs such as Alcoholics Anonymous. The basis of the Twelve Step program is to emotionally give your self up to a higher power. Even if you are not a religious person, by reciting the Serenity Prayer ("God grant me the Serenity to accept the things I cannot change, Courage to change the things that I can and the Wisdom to know the difference."), millions of people have attested that they have become more relaxed and "centred." "It has made a huge difference for me in not only coping with what I can't control with our son, like some of his behaviours, but also has improved my general outlook on life." When you dismiss the power struggles in your life and turn to "whatever happens, happens, it is not in my hands," you almost instantaneously feel better because you are no longer fighting with yourself (and others) to obtain or regain control.

This is also true with another method taken from the book *The Four Agreements*, which discusses committing yourself to these basic beliefs:

Be impeccable with your word

Don't take anything personally

Don't make assumptions

Always do your best.

When I first read this book, it struck me that it was almost as if these statements were written specifically for parents of affected children. I personally have found that daily review of these affirmations has clearly made a positive difference in reducing my stress level, particularly with things I simply have no control over. It inspires me to let go of the feeling of "I need to have control" over everything and to focus on doing the best I can in whatever I do.

What is success anyway?

How do we establish our expectations for success? Some days my idea of success is that I was able to leave one French fry on the plate instead of eating them all. You have to determine what is really important to you and what is reasonably realistic about what you can *all* do in your family. For example, we all have the dreaded daily "TO DO" list. If your list resembles the length of your monthly cash register receipt for groceries, you may want to try renaming your list to imply more achievable goals. It's all in the lingo: change the spirit of a menacing "TO DO" list to "If I get anything done today at all, let it be this . . ." You will not only prioritize more effectively but feel great at the end of the day because you met your goals by breaking them down. It's the same theory that some of us use when we exercise. Instead of being focused and consequently overwhelmed by "fifty-five minutes to go," piecemeal it down to five-minute intervals and congratulate yourself each time you meet that goal. Once you have accomplished striking one item off your new list, you might actually have more energy to complete one or two other things on some days!

Another example of finding perspective and re-evaluating success is to compare yourselves with other families; for instance, how long their kids are living at home. There is currently a trend in North America where young people are not leaving the family nest until their mid-to-late 20's, or they leave home only to return as soon as they've run out of Kraft Dinner. We encourage parents of FASD adults to realize that they likely need to stay at home longer, and get this - so does your neighbour's kid! Often when you're consumed with finding direction or answers for your child, you don't notice (or aren't told) that other people's kids screw up. Many do so with flair, like being brought home by the police. All kids at some point do things without thinking. I recall one Christmas, a colleague of mine had gone into her freezer the morning of December 24th to discover that her 17-year-old son had eaten all but half a dozen of the 15 dozen cookies she needed for a dinner for 25, a work function, and holiday entertaining. She made me stay at the office with her because she was sure if she went home before her husband got there, she would strangle her own flesh and blood until he choked up at least half the cookies. Realistically, in comparison with the rest of the world, your family is merely somewhere smack in the middle of dysfunction junction. Believe in your child and the rest will come.

Appreciating tragedy

A gentle reminder: When we are feeling in a funk about our own lives, consider the reality that it could be much worse. It certainly does put things into perspective. Sadly, real-life stories of unthinkable tragedies are abundant in the media: accounts of mothers whose children were all murdered by their ex-husbands, or a father who, while on a trip to find a new home, learns that his wife and six children have perished in a house fire. Some families deal with serious and excruciatingly painful illnesses that are often terminal. It is difficult to know whether we will ever be able to truly realise the extent of the destruction and the ramifications thereof in the horrors of September 11th or the Asian Tsunami. One thing is for sure, these catastrophes have turned us from the "me" generation into a society that generously poured out not only money and time, but also insurmountable emotional support to those in need. It brought hope to their future and ours. No matter how difficult a day can be, honouring the survivors of such heartbreaking experiences will inspire you to feel grateful for what you have. Let's not forget to always count our blessings, especially our loved ones.

Chapter Ten

Compassion fatigue - who is caring for the caregiver?

I had a home visit once with a lady who was a single parent of two teenagers. As we were drinking our tea, her son blew in through the door in a flurry of airborne gloves, papers and boots, obviously caught up in a heated argument with his backpack. Before she could move, he yelled out: "Mom! Can I get a movie? Can I get a movie? Can I get a movie?" She immediately walked towards him, touched his shoulder and pointed, saying, "Michael, put your jacket on the hook." She waited; "now put your boots on the matt;" done. Then, "Please pick up all of the papers and put them on the kitchen table" (demonstrating the direction). She finished with "Ok, now go up to your room and read your comics quietly" (finger over the lips to cue quietly). He was half way up the stairs when he bolted back down and zoomed his face towards her, nose to nose, asking, "Mom, can I have a movie?" "No, Michael, not now. Go to your room and read comics, and we will get a movie tonight." With light speed he traveled upstairs, and she chose to ignore what sounded like the plumbing being replaced. She attempted to catch her breath to sit down, and before her bottom could squish the seat cushion, Michael bounded down the narrow stairwell, all knees and elbows much like a big puppy. I swear I saw paint chips fly off the walls. "Mom, can I have a movie?" I looked up at the clock and determined that this had now extended to a 28 minute calamity. She stood up, spun him around, and sent him, yet again, to his room. As she plopped into the chair and reached for her teacup, she innocently looked at me and said, "You know, I don't know why I've been feeling so tired lately!"

One thing I've learned about parents of kids with

disabilities is that they are also the caregivers to the entire world. One can usually find them simultaneously caring for more than one child, a cat, stray dogs, other people's kids; they are the chef of the brownies for the bake sale, supporter of other families, driver of the hockey team, volunteer for the church fair, director of the school play; they are looking after aging parents and making soup for a sick friend. Oh yeah, and they manage to squeeze in housework and a day job, too. If this even remotely describes you, I have one piece of strategic, well researched, official and intellectually sound advice - quit it. Not everything, but I ask you, in all the minutes in a day, what are you doing for YOU? And don't say you get to sleep at least five hours a night; that doesn't count. Read a magazine article lately? I didn't think so. Listen, if you constantly feel like you are in a rush to get things done - SLOW DOWN! Start delegating, reducing, alternating, substituting, handing over some of your duties, then repeat after me: "**No! No,** I cannot volunteer at bingo. **No,** I am not making an extra trip because it is more convenient for someone else. **No,** I can't argue with you right now because I'm late for my first hair appointment in five years, and **no,** nobody is going to be traumatized for life by wearing a store bought Halloween costume this year." Give yourself a pat on the back for all that you do, and know that you make a wonderful difference for others. Then ease into making *you* a priority with the ultimate goal being to simplify your life. Let's face it - parenting when you're pooped likely doesn't reflect your best work. Take some time to think about this. If you discover that you've become too indispensable, gradually make some changes in finding true balance in your life between doing for others and doing for yourself. You're worth it, and so are they.

Looking after you

Next in order, you should make a doctor's appointment

because, believe me, you are probably more physically tired out than you realize. What often happens to parents at the time of the diagnosis is that countless medical professionals are assigned to the child, but what about the parents? Sometimes the natural stages of denial, grief, loss and acceptance are lost in the mix for parents as the spotlight is fixed on the child. See your physician to make sure that your health is up to snuff, both physically and mentally. One of the most common side effects of raising children with disabilities that goes totally unnoticed by parents is chronic fatigue. I know a woman who was so preoccupied with environmental stress that she was astounded to find out that her exhaustion was exacerbated because she was in full-blown menopause, and was too busy to notice! Today's world is fraught with anxiety, tension, over-stimulation, excess, and trepidation that often exceed what any of us can cope with. Depression is much more commonplace, particularly in this caregiver patient population and for genuinely understandable reasons. Medication *for you,* and not just your child, might be a viable option if you fit the bill. See your doctor and let him or her know how you're feeling so you can talk openly about your choices to invigorate your overall health and wellness.

And the Academy Award goes to . . .

There is a scene in the movie *A League of Their Own* where Tom Hanks is extremely frustrated with a player who keeps making the same error over and over again. As his screaming has not worked, it is strongly suggested to him that he deal with her by staying as calm as he can, and explaining his concerns in a soft, understanding voice. This turns out to be so gruelling for him that he starts physically shaking and sputtering, and his eyes take on a shape that is almost indescribable while he is trying to talk to her about her chronic mistake. Trust me, it is well worth the watch. So how do you manage to make such sweeping change of basically your personality? It's hard to create normalcy in an atypical situation, but there will be situations worth putting on your game face for. As we know, many kids are quite impressionable just by your voice inflection and physical demeanour. A perfect example of this is a mom who, right before they have to leave, exuberantly leaps towards her daughter with a big hug and smile and quips: "Hey Linda! Let's go to the dentist AND THEN FOR BURGER AND A MILKSHAKE! Her daughter gleefully replies, "OK!!!" (essentially because all she heard was two words, burger and milkshake, and saw a big smile on Mom's face). Is it sneaky? Yes. Manipulative? Sure. Do we care? Not really. If it works, do it and then be sure to arrange your seat next to Johnny Depp on academy award night.

Affirmative language

Language paradigm shifts have been well documented with regard to behaviours often attached to FASD, such as moving from "hyperactive" to "energetic." It has been my experience that we have nicely adapted this strategy with our kids, but not for ourselves. HELLO! The first step in really creating positive change and emotional comfort has to start *with you*. There is a marked difference between telling yourself, "I must be a lousy parent because I can't control my child's behaviour" to "I have the strength and courage to accept the things I cannot change and do my best." If you anticipate pleasure in a day, close your eyes and be thankful; it's more likely to turn out that way.

The transformation from negative-based talk to positive connotations has a most compelling effect. Motivational speakers, particularly in finance, suggest that you draft an affirmative statement that echoes **your** ultimate goals, dreams or wishes, and then repeat it several times a day. It can be anything from emotional or health aspirations to money. For example, "I am happy, healthy and save 200 hundred dollars a month," and then visualize yourself *being* your goals. Envision yourself smiling and laughing, in good health, skipping down the beach at Waikiki. Repeat it to yourself out loud and/or write it down ten times. Do this at least twice a day, when you're in the doctor's office, before you go to bed, or right before a meeting that you anticipate may make your hair stand on end. After the meeting isn't a bad idea either. It takes about two whole minutes a day, so don't go to the "I have no time" alibi; start making yourself a priority in your day. Over time you will achieve your goals and then begin to reach for new dreams. Through a life change of accentuating the positive and eliminating the negative, personal success will be yours to enjoy.

Date night Do's and Don'ts

The focal point of this exercise is to act as if you're on a date, with yourself and/or a partner. If you can't seem to squeeze this in at least once a month, re-read this book five times.

<u>Rules for parents with partners:</u>

Do's: Turn off the cell phones, get to know each other, notice how attractive your partner is, see a funny movie or play, have a pizza and a beer, play darts, go for a long scenic walk, see some friends that make you laugh, get a hotel room (if you can't remember what to do in this department, at least get some sleep), go shopping and buy something just for the two of you, hold hands, read together in a quiet space with a good cup of coffee, get a massage, take a one-session class together in something new, go to the batting cage, share a big piece of chocolate cake, play a game of cards, thank each other, be grateful for what you have, be proud of yourselves for your accomplishments. Have some fun. Get some exercise. To rekindle your relationship, do something that you both liked to do before you had kids. Find yourselves again.

Don'ts:

*Warning! A therapy session does not count as a date. No sore point issues are to be raised, by discussion, barbs, innuendo or body language. Negative self-talk is out. No kid conversations are allowed. No work-related chatter. Unless it has to do with any of the **Do** rules, it is not allowed.

<u>Rules for parents who choose no partner:</u>

Turn off the cell phone, get to know yourself, notice how attractive you are, see a funny movie or play, have a pizza and a beer, play darts, go for a long scenic walk, see some friends that make you laugh, get a hotel room (you probably could use a warm tub and some sleep), go shopping and buy something just for you, hold someone's hand, read in a quiet space with a good cup of coffee, get a massage, take a one-session class in something new, go to the batting cage, have a big piece of chocolate cake, play a game of solitaire, thank yourself and be grateful for what you have, be proud of your accomplishments. Have some fun. Get some exercise. Do something that you liked to do before you had kids to rekindle that feeling. Find yourself again.

Respite

Personally I've never been partial to the term "respite"; it typically implies a breather or relief, as opposed to actual babysitting, which basically translated means taking care of another short person. Perhaps we could rename it "shared-care," as it has a more exact and upbeat undertone. Further, there seems to be a negative connotation attached to respite for some reason: Our societal conventions imply that if you have a children, you should be responsible for them no matter what. This concern is particularly amplified for adoptive parents in that "We chose to adopt and it is our responsibility to keep them full time and not rely on others." Foster families have also commented, "because we are paid care providers, we shouldn't need respite," or that their agency may have implied that they are in some way ineffectual or "greedy" parents if they ask for paid respite on top of the two dollars and ten cents a week salary they receive for five children. Birth parents may be consumed with guilt: "I did this to my child, and I need to take responsibility now. I don't deserve any help." These feelings can also be made worse because parents are afraid that their child will be taken away from them, and sadly, that is a reality for some parents, particularly if they are still fighting addictions. In any event, in situations where parents are reluctant to utilize shared-care it is usually for very good reasons.

There are a couple of ways to view the situation: not only do the parents need a break from their child, but *they need a break from us* because the stress levels in the home are likely by that time off the Richter scale. In the long run it may prove most advantageous for your child to have established regular shared-care as a matter of course (a brief holiday, "just what we do on a regular basis") as opposed to waiting until you are in crisis mode. This way your child is accustomed to visiting somewhere else on occasion, instead of feeling like a "bad" kid when asked to leave because everyone has blown a fuse. Some parents have become frustrated and I agree with them when told by others, "you **have** to take respite." It is well documented that respite reduces exit rates from foster care and other family situations, and is instrumental in reducing stress for both child and parents. However, shared-care is something that should be available to parents when and how **they** request it, because there are numerous reasons that they may not feel comfortable doing so.

Due to central nervous system dysfunction, many affected individuals have tremendous difficulty with change and find it extremely difficult to adapt. I recall a colleague of mine telling me a story of when she was a little girl. Her mother became ill, and her father placed her with a neighbour lady for a week. She vividly remembered how even though the lady was kind to her, it wasn't the same bed, she cooked differently than her mother, the bed time was not what she was used to, and she was nervous because she didn't know what to expect. All of us tend to act differently when we feel we are in a situation we cannot control or anticipate. For people with physiologically based dysfunction, this type of experience may be drastically amplified, resulting in the presentation of erratic, unstable behaviours and making it more difficult for the child and family than if they had not used shared-care. The bottom line is that funding must be made readily available to families so they are able to decide on what is most beneficial for them. Like any family, they may find some months better than others and they may want to stay together during such timeframes. Those individuals that don't live in the home need to respect the family's shared-care decisions.

Parenting as a family

There are several factors to reflect on when parenting as a family. Due to the nature of FASD, it is not uncommon for parents to have a tendency to blame themselves or their spouse when nothing seems to be working in correcting unwanted behaviours. The friction between parents can become extreme with constant disagreement over whose technique is right and whose is wrong. "My husband could just not accept that our son was not going to respond to his father's method of parenting. He was embarrassed by our son and personalized his actions as intentionally trying to undermine him." Regrettably, some families have fallen casualty to divorce. This is especially true if their child was not yet diagnosed or only recently diagnosed in their teens when the parenting patterns and emotions were long since established. It's tough to change gears at that point, and, as with any good parenting model, it is critical that both of you are together in team parenting.

The most successful families I know have, upon receiving a diagnosis, grieved for the fact that their child has a life-long medical issue, researched the disability, asked for as much assistance as they could find, and rolled up their sleeves and made a short- and long-term plan for their entire family. They take turns and they balance the workload in the household as best they can. Families can support each other and make themselves a priority by getting outside help, like a cleaning lady, even if they're not made of money. They adjust their expectations. They take holidays, sometimes without their kids. They treat themselves to a night out, and make sure they spend one-on-one time with their other children so those don't feel left out. They appreciate how difficult it is for their other children to cope with a sister or brother that always gets into personal things and seems to be the focal point of the family (taking up much of parental time with medical appointments, school meetings or therapy sessions). Most of all, they are organized and have mastered the balance of dividing time for their family and themselves as equally as possible. They see the humour in life and appreciate that the glass is half full.

How do we get everyone on board?

Getting everyone in the family together on understanding the implications of the disability and what it means to the patient and them can be accomplished in an enjoyable and cohesive way. In our neck of the woods, we have a family potluck dinner gathering where a FASD support person comes out to the house with a PowerPoint presentation called the "Diagnostic Interpretation of Abilities Session (DIAS ©)." The family invites anyone that they feel would benefit from an information session regarding their child's specific abilities. The meeting often includes extended family, friends, teachers, classroom assistants, therapists, social workers, sports coaches and shared-care providers. Alternative arrangements are made for the patients, as it is not considered appropriate to have them in attendance. They are provided the same type of presentation, only it is designed to explain their diagnosis in conjunction with their learning style and is also strength focused. This allows the participants to freely ask questions regarding the diagnosis and discuss strategy development in all areas of the patient's life, such as health, academics and recreation. These sessions encompass a collection of information gathered from the parents' assessment of their child, medical documentation and teacher observations. We identify any physical abnormalities and how they may translate to behaviours. As a group, we conjure up a list of strengths and positive attributes of patients and examine and discuss their cognitive (processing) abilities. Then we use the **OBD 3 Step Plan of Action!** and work through the top two or three behaviours of concern. We develop ideas and strategies for everyone to use by focusing on what the patient can do and by acknowledging any limitations. Sessions are updated as many times as necessary, for example, for changes to a new school or grade level, residential placement, or introduction of a new shared-care provider.

Most importantly, we do it together. The emphasis is on realising that the affected individual's eyes do not see what we see, and ears do not hear what we hear. Sometimes, particularly for siblings, we do an actual demonstration about how it *feels* to be the affected person by having everyone wear a large tissue-paper hat, four layers of clothing, flickering the lights on and off rapidly, and blaring the television and radio at the same time. I get them to hold a personal item with bulky mittens on to have them simulate how easy it is for their brother to break their things without knowing it. I'll have them taste something bitter to prove he's not just a fussy eater if they are mad because "He doesn't deserve special treatment" at mealtime. It is far easier to change your ways if you can relate, and you can't change what you don't understand and accept. Once things are explained in plain English and in terms that everyone can understand, the impact can be astounding, and hugely instrumental in evolving approaches for everyone.

Support groups

Many parents find support groups a tremendous help, not only in exchanging ideas, but in talking to other parents who can relate to a very special circumstance. Global FASD Parent Support groups have also been very proactive in advocating for improvements to government services and ground breaking in the area of public awareness. You may want to consider a support group where the members are the same type of parent (birth parent, adoptive parent, foster parent or kinship care) because the issues for these respective groups are considerably different. This is of particular importance for birth mothers, as unfortunately, there have been incidents of other frustrated parents venting their anger about women who drink during pregnancy without realizing that a birth mom was in the group. All parents have the right to verbalize their feelings in a safe, structured, supportive environment where the goals are to learn from each other and move forward in a positive direction. I always suggest that groups start and end meetings with a humorous or heart-warming story, joke or sentiment to help keep things in a positive perspective.

Families affected by FASD have a greater chance of experiencing . . .

A Sudden Infant Death

Shaken Baby syndrome

Attachment problems

Embarrassment

Resentment

Allegations of ineffectual parenting

Strained or termination of friendships

Depression

Marital discourse

Familial Dysfunction

Feelings of inadequacy

Loss of things of value

Employment disruption

Sibling rivalry

Confusion

Chronic fatigue

Numerous medical appointments

Necessity for medications

Inappropriate planning

Unrealistic expectations

Anger and frustration

Loss of control

Infinite parenting expectations

Higher risk for criminal justice involvement

Repeated attempts at therapy

Increased possibility of raising grandchildren

Termination of guardianship

Loss of decision-making powers

Feeling unheard

Low self-esteem

Guilt

Fear of inappropriate parenting

Stress

Health issues

Increased risk of self-medicating

Financial strain

Grief and loss of a "normal" life

Us giving up on them

AND an even greater chance of experiencing . . .

A different way to look at the world

Holding the world's record in projectile vomiting

Learning how to be more patient

Maximizing our inner strength and potential

Having more belly laughs

Gently being reminded to be kind

An expanded knowledge base of colourful language

Bringing out the activist in us

Being reminded to never to take things for granted

Inspiring ingenuity

Getting the creative juices flowing

Fine-tuning our organizational skills

Enlightening us to our own personal spirituality

Encouraging us to change our staunch ways

Introducing us to the roller-coaster ride of life

Teaching us to dream more often

Motivating us to learn new ways to communicate with
your spouse

Bringing us together

Educating us that respecting them and ourselves is
paramount to happiness

Giving us more reasons to shop

Proving to us that a lack of fear is not always a bad thing

Kindling relationships with people we may otherwise
never have met

Motivating us to try new things

Being unselfish

Realizing that control isn't all it's cracked up to be

Spurring us on to a crash course in being assertive

Helping us realize that there is always someone who has
it worse off than we do

Giving us perspective on friendships

Keeping us humble

Making us experts in the inner workings of public
education systems

Finding the silver lining

Exemplifying to us appreciation of how important
balance is in our lives

Appreciating who our good friends are

Taking more risks

Finding positives in everything we do

Getting us involved in our community

Realizing that there are some really terrific people who
care in the world

Showing us what true love really is

Chapter Eleven

Transitions into adulthood

Some Social Services agencies contract Youth Workers or Mentorship Programs, and as suggested earlier, they can be very beneficial to a child, youth or adult with disabilities. However, for children and youth who have boundary issues and require role modeling to assist them, what better way to confuse them than to have a stranger show up at their house and let them take them out on an activity to get to know each other. Let's face it - this would rarely occur in another family setting, but because they are in foster care, these children are sometimes introduced to different standards of intervention set out by well-meaning government agencies that foster parents are expected to comply with. Furthermore, inadequate training of staff can lead to "double messages" for some youth. For example, a young man whose parents forbid him to wear his baseball cap in a restaurant did so because his Youth Worker was wearing his. In the extreme and rare case, insufficient training can be deadly. Unfortunately, this has been proven in a case where a group home staff member was killed while working with a very complicated affected young person.

We have clearly established that many affected children and youth are prone to mimicking what is around them, such as use of speech, dress, social behaviours, and most importantly, what they see on television, videos and the Internet. For persons who have such difficulties differentiating between fact and fantasy and/or have experienced *severe* childhood maltreatment or may not be aware of their actual strength or force, the constant daily bombardment of violence further complicates the parenting process. Programming is getting worse on prime time television and radio, with bare breasts being flaunted, combined with the sexual innuendo of "pelvic grinding"; vulgar and rude language spoken at whim; and a sense that "I will offend people because I can." Kids are sponges for what they are exposed, and media visuals have clearly contributed to this generation's confusion. Sadly, it is the mentality of disrespect for one another in this generation, like no other, that takes a toll on our beliefs and complicates parenting methodology. In order to teach our principles to our children we must examine this issue and address how we will respond to this assault of impertinence, and recognize that it affects us all. Even though we have become desensitized to a degree, it is for us to realize that affected individuals do not have a "filter" and need our guidance to understand the difference. Parents may be required to be more sensitive and reticent about what their teenager watches with regard to television, movies and violent video games, because some individuals may be at higher risk to mimic actions without realizing the consequences of those actions.

This is certainly **not** to suggest that if disabled youth watch a T.V. murder they will go out and commit one of their own. However, there must be discussions of the differences between reality and fantasy, with any required monitoring based on the individual's *perceptions* of these activities. In the event that your child is obviously becoming over-stimulated or aggressive after somewhat violent visual interactions, it may be a signal to decrease or terminate the activity. Respect for other people and for life itself obviously needs to be reintroduced into our current societal standards.

Supported independent living models

A major mistake in managing adolescents and young adults is to expect and graduate independence based on their actual age and not on their *overall* executive functioning abilities. In some cases parents have accessed out-of-home Supported Independent Living Programs that proved disastrous and culminated with their child promptly becoming involved in the world of secondary disabilities, such as substance abuse, criminal activities, depression, weight gain or loss, becoming more aggressive, and/or continually running away. This is not to suggest that these programs are not suitable for your child; rather, one has to choose the agency that has experience with Persons with Disabilities in general and that provides staff training and support in working with individuals with a variety of forms of brain dysfunction. Staff members are usually educated in rehabilitation, which promotes an understanding that clientele will require modifications to their environment. Further, they realize that persons with any form of brain injury can be very difficult to live with at times. Look for an agency that agrees to implement the same structure, routine and supervision that you provided in your home. Again, you are the expert in your child, knowing what works and what doesn't (what's been tried but proved unsuccessful), and those venturing into a long-term commitment with your family should welcome this advice.

Employment opportunities

Consider that your child may not be geared for a conventional career. ADHD people tend to be creative in the way that they think, and in some cases this has led to earning big money. They are usually risk takers and that may be something that really works out in the long run. Encourage and allow them the visionary freedom to come up with a potential calling. Other individuals may require precise routine and consistent repetition of duties in their workday. This would be the type of job that entails little to no transitions (changes or surprises) to cope with. It is the same work, every day, all day. Talk to young adults about which type of work they might be best at. Remind them of strengths and that it's a good idea to explore what things they may not care for in a job (like getting up early in the morning). This will help to guide your adult child into a work setting more suited to his or her abilities and reduce the chance of frustration or failure.

Some families support their teenagers in finding summer employment with the view to prepare them for adult responsibilities. To ensure their safety, I highly recommend that you consider all aspects and potential ramifications of the job they are intending to apply for. A classic example: Here in Calgary, Alberta, Canada, every July we host the world famous Calgary Exhibition and Stampede. It's a blast! There are a rodeo, carnival and rides of all kinds, fair competitions and exhibits, as well as every kind of food under the sun. The entire city is in party-mode for 10 days straight, everyone dresses in western garb, and there is something for all age groups. One little guy I know is doing pretty well in the "mutton busting" competition where he sits on a sheep and hangs on for dear life - it's a hoot! Naturally, when the Stampede comes to town temporary jobs are aplenty and teenagers are in great demand for food service, ticket sales, showing people around, working in the barns, etc. Sounds like a great opportunity, right? Short-term job (10 days) and various work experiences to choose from with a regular work schedule. You may be willing to drive teens there and back to make sure they get there on time. Wrong. The problem here is that, unfortunately, what can come with travelling carnivals is travelling pimps, drug dealers, and unsavoury characters that see a perfect opportunity to target and entice teenagers into their world. Unless you are guaranteed that a responsible adult (like you) is at their side for the entirety of their shift to protect them from slick predators, don't be afraid to just say no (the "because-I-said-so" kind of no!) Always keep in mind that once your child is exposed to and absorbs inappropriate behaviours it is harder to intervene. As much as possible, **prevent** possible opportunities for children to be enticed, as they likely won't know how to get themselves out of it. In situations like this, be their eyes, ears and intuition.

It seems that the most common problem in keeping a job for FASD patients is always getting there on time, if at all. Please don't be discouraged or feel that your young person is just being lazy or not wanting to work; it is most likely due to one or a combination of the following issues:

1) The patient has chronic physiological problems with the sleep/awake cycle and has little to no control over when he or she will tire or "feel" that it is time to wake up. Many affected individuals do not possess an "internal clock" as a direct result of the damage to the Central Nervous System. This makes it *physically* very difficult to wake up and be refreshed at certain times of the day as dictated by the individual's particular sleep/awake cycle.

2) Many individuals have memory problems and struggle to remember dates or appointments. This can be exacerbated especially if the job entails a varied schedule of when to be there.

3) Some patients become overwhelmed (easily tired and stressed) and may feel that the instructions or actual job task has become too challenging. In many instances affected individuals are not able to verbalise their concerns to the employer because of difficulties with communication skills.

4) Due to the nature of brain injury/dysfunction, patients often have difficulty sticking to anything for long periods of time and appear to "give up" more easily than their peers.

There are many ways to assist young people in these areas in order to reduce the incidence of sporadic employment:

1a) Encourage your young adult to look for a job that starts later in the day or at night.

2a) Avoid employment opportunities where the scheduling of workdays is not consistent.

3a) Prepare the young person *before* they get the job by role-playing and practicing situations that are likely to occur. (What do you do if you don't understand the directions?) Together, write out on paper potential concerns, or use whatever method has proven effective for your child to communicate a point. Discuss the possibility of informing the employer of concerns, perhaps through a suggestion box or a daily/weekly review, to keep the lines of communication open. Regularly review with teens/adults their level of job satisfaction and suggest that they also use this strategy to tell the boss how much they enjoy the job and working together.

4a) Come to terms with the fact that things have changed in our society from only valuing a 45 year career at the same company, to a culture where it is quite acceptable to have several occupations. The previous stigma of "not keeping a job" is no longer as apparent as years ago; we now appreciate that it is not for everybody. You and your adult child should not be ashamed of "sporadic employment"; rather, accept it as a chance to learn all sorts of trades or vocations and to have many new, exciting experiences. Persons with Disabilities government-funded programs usually allow for occasional or irregular employment and do not typically disqualify their ongoing pension, so don't worry.

Supported work environments

There is a range of programming available to persons that qualify for disabilities assistance. Some services provide daily one-on-one supervision at the job site by a staff. For example, my guy's day-staff worker (she is there five days a week for consistency) travels with him to and from the job and stands by if he needs assistance. Other vocational employment programs have a low ratio of workers to staff (three to five workers to one staff). In the event that your adult does not qualify for disabilities funding, you can organize additional support by providing the employer some basic facts regarding the individual's abilities. You may also be able to find a Job Coach by investigating government programs or through the community via Volunteer Programs. Let them know what your needs are and someone like a retiree or a student may be available to help out. Again, they only need to know that there are learning problems (brain dysfunction) and not specifically that your child is alcohol-affected. Any and all staff working with your adult should be strictly advised likewise. Take a look at service clubs and apply for grants for assistance. You'd be surprised how many good and decent people are out there willing to lend assistance if asked. (For a video presentation on this topic try *FAS Forward: A Fresh Look at Fetal Alcohol Syndrome*. (The information is in the reference section at the back of the book.) For kids that want to complete a secondary education, check into colleges that provide additional supports to students with various disabilities. They may be able to assist your child with a host of supports including a student "buddy," end-of-the-day review of assignments, and counselling services (on a bad day) if required.

Sexual activity and birth control

I've noticed that every time I bring up this topic in a group there is an immediate and collective cringe especially amongst parents. We know that for individuals with central nervous system dysfunction, attention deficit disorders, impulsivity problems and lack of inhibition, the word "YIKES" seems to automatically spring to mind when related to sexual activity. These issues singly, or in combination, imply that FASD-affected persons would be at higher risk for unplanned pregnancies, and **they are.** There is no one magic answer, but there are definitely things you can do to reduce the chance of becoming grandparents well before your skin starts sagging:

- As much as possible **know where your kids are!** It takes a lot of time and effort to achieve this, but when you feel tired and start to wane, weigh the alternatives - the baby shower thrown by *your* grandmother, three a.m. feedings, diapers, etc. Enlist as many "watch-dogs" as you can to help out on a regular basis to give you some piece of mind.

- When your child is not with you, **know whom they are with** and make sure that the **adults in the situation are aware that enhanced supervision is a must.** It is a good idea to have a conversation with the parents of opposite sex peers as soon as they are technically able to conceive. Although it can seem embarrassing to discuss particularly with people you don't know, remind yourself of the potential outcome (whaaaaah!).

- **Check in with your child as to whether he or she is in fact being supervised well while visiting a friend's home.** In the event you discover that the other parent has run out for groceries, leaving the hormones unattended, suggest that the friend come to your home instead. As most of us know, getting pregnant takes a total of about four seconds, so any amount of unsupervised time has baby-making potential.

- **Start regular conversations** with your child about relationships **before he or she reaches puberty.** There are oodles of books and videos designed specifically for educating individuals with various abilities in sexual interactions and birth control. Role playing and repeatedly practicing what to do if someone touches them is a terrific way to make the reaction hopefully "automatic." If you make these regular and ongoing conversations, your child has a better chance of remembering what to do.

- I know I'm going to get letters about this, but here it is anyway - **consider getting your daughters on birth control as soon as they start their menstrual cycles.** If you make it a regular part of life early on, birth control does not become an issue when they are adults; it is simply what they are used to doing. Males require regular coaching on using a condom. I know what you're thinking: the probability of them actually remembering protection in the heat of the moment is a stretch, but repetition of information is better than nothing. It may also be a good idea to role-play a discussion with their partner about whether she is on birth control, and if she isn't, that is a signal (reminder) to stop or, at the very least, use a condom.

- In the event you sense that your child is "warming up" to the idea of entering into a sexual relationship, encourage him or her to have a discussion with the intended. Even though you may have to endure exaggerated eye rolling and a drawn out "Daaaaaaadddd!" a plan with appropriate questions and/or concerns (on paper) should be in place because, let's face it, they're probably going to do it anyway. Rehearsal is the vehicle that we all use to get through an awkward conversation, and once we practice, it becomes much easier to do and we are more likely to follow through.

Peer supports

Try to be cautious of reverse segregation by discouraging friendships with other FASD youth or adults (if they are healthy and have appropriate supports). Your child may find much in common with such individuals, and the relationship may help them feel more comfortable knowing they aren't the only one with FASD. On the other hand, they may conjure friendships with people who have no form of disability or have another form of brain dysfunction and get along famously because they still have much in common. Guide your child in seeking out positive relationships while respecting the choices as much as you can.

Mental health problems

The Secondary Disabilities Study completed by Dr. Ann Steissguth revealed that 90% of the FASD-affected individuals studied presented with mental health problems. We now know that depression is by far the most common mental health issue to date for alcohol-affected persons. Not coincidently, for individuals with other various forms of brain injury or dysfunction, depression is usually the number one mental health issue. Consequently, you should anticipate that, at some point in life, your child might experience some form of depression. This can be displayed in many ways, not only the telltale signs of withdrawing, isolating themselves, verbalising or writing down that they intend to hurt themselves or God forbid, actually do. *Depression can also take the form of anger and aggression, which unfortunately can be misdiagnosed. Some patients confuse "mad" with "sad" and require treatment accordingly.

This is one more reason to seek out a professional that has expertise in FASD *specifically*. Be sure that the Psychiatrist, Psychologist or Social Worker believes in the existing medical diagnosis under the range of Fetal Alcohol Spectrum Disorders. If they don't, go elsewhere. The chosen professional may suggest medication, and as with the rest of the millions of people currently taking anti-depression and/or anti-anxiety medications, everyone responds differently. Accurate assessment, recognition and support of mental health issues are key for all affected individuals and particularly for those who have been adopted, because some mental health issues can be hereditary. As with anything else, *some* FASD patients are diagnosed with FASD and with other co-morbidities such as schizophrenia, bi-polar disorder or obsessive-compulsive disorder. Some just have FASD. It's kind of like the chicken and the egg thing as far as what comes first. Nonetheless, in either case, it is still the correct identification and understanding of the issue that are critical to appropriate treatment.

As with mental health issues, some families seem to be predisposed to addictions whether by hereditary disposition and/or by environmental determinants. It is of great importance to make your child aware of the fact that, either way, **affected individuals have a higher risk of addictions to substances** than their peers. There are many ways to approach this issue, such as having your adolescent speak with a doctor, have regular discussions in your home about alcohol and/or drug use, and most importantly, model appropriate and responsible behaviour when it comes to alcohol and drug use. An excellent resource in this area is *Tough Kids and Substance Abuse - A drug awareness program for children and adolescents* *with ARND, FAS, FAE and cognitive disabilities* (details in the Reference section of this book). It provides visuals, links the patient's feelings and emotions with alcohol and/or drug use, and is geared to a learning style that suits many FASD-affected individuals. Again, additional supervision may be required, but you can also circumvent potential addictions problems by teaching them appropriate relaxation methods. One of the main problems for persons with central nervous system dysfunction problems is that they often feel very physically and mentally tense and overwhelmed by life in general. Even a brief trial of self-medicating with alcohol and/or drugs can hook them quite quickly, particularly alcohol and marijuana because these are a form of *relaxants.* It takes them away, numbs the pain of being different, and gives them false courage. This is why early education, making them busy with positive, structured activities, building in self-esteem boosters and being honest about their respective situation are mainstays in preventing a problem with substance abuse before it starts.

In the event children have succumbed to the powers of alcohol and/or drugs, again it is recommended that they engage in individual treatment with an addictions specialist who has training in FASD. You may also want to try introducing them to the Letter Therapy that we talked about earlier. Some kids have found it very helpful to write a letter about how they feel to their birth parent(s), to you, to a higher power and, sometimes, to themselves. A journal can be kept by either writing in a scribbler or talking into a recording device, and it may prove quite helpful to your child on a regular basis to keep track of moods and patterns of feelings like depression or frustration, but most of all, in times of trouble. Many of my female patients also record their menstrual cycles so that they can anticipate cranky days ahead of time and plan for these accordingly, such as by taking extra care of themselves. Last but not least, you may want to try writing letters to each other. Stick to rules by only stating feelings and not judgements, and start and end the letters on a positive note. You never know, it just might open the doors to a deeper understanding and release for both of you.

Evaluating residential programs

The transition from home to a new residence can be a frightening experience for everyone. On the other hand, don't feel too bad if your kid is packed up and ready to go four weeks before he or she is scheduled to move out. When shopping for a residential placement for your adult child, here is list of questions to consider:

- Are the program's goals consistent with your family's goals for your adult child?

- Is the amount and type of supervision suitable to your child's needs?

- Is the program willing to provide transportation?

- Are staff specifically trained in FASD, and if not, are they willing to be?

- Do staff issue medications and ensure they are taken appropriately?

- Is the residence located in a safe neighbourhood?

- What are the expectations regarding household chores and curfews?

- What is the procedure if your child breaks a rule?

- Is there a choice of roommate, and does the roommate have more complex problems than your child?

- Are the rules flexible enough to suit your child's needs?

- Is the transition time from home to the placement flexible? (Can your child stay over on weekends at first, or does he or she have to move in immediately?)

- Does the environment promote appropriate behaviour? (Inquire as to any behaviours of concern among potential roommates.)

- Is the residence well connected with other agencies and recreational programs designed for persons with disabilities?

- What does the residence offer for recreation? How often is it available? Is it negotiable, or does your adult child have to attend?

- Will the residence respect your adult child's "alone" time?

- What kind of contact will the residential staff have with you in the long term?

- Who will be responsible for money management?

- Are the phones blocked for unauthorized long distance phone calls?

- Who is responsible for nutrition, menu planning and cooking?

- Who is responsible for taking your child to the doctor?

- What is the policy with regard to visitors (of **both** sexes) and supervision?

In order to reduce the stress of transitioning as much as possible, it is important to include adult children in the process. Have them do up a list of questions and include these in the interviews and walk-through of the potential household. Suggest ways that they may want to decorate their space and make a shopping list of things they will need (new pots, dishes, bedding), and encourage them to do their own environmental check of lighting and sound. The more control they feel they have over the decision to move on, the more likely they will adapt to the new setting. Continue to assess the placement once they are moved in, and be sure to advise all staff of any quirks that might translate to disruptive behaviour. For example, if they sit in a wet bathing suit for too long, they may just peel it off on the spot (public place or not). Residential and employment support staff must be educated not only on FASD in general, but in the small things that, in combination, can lead to huge misunderstandings and unnecessary disaster.

If your adult child does not qualify for adult residential services, you could consider several options:

- If you have the money, purchase a condo/apartment/small house and find a roommate to share expenses. Depending on your adult child's needs, make regular visits and enlist him or her in visitation services through various volunteer agencies.

- Advertise to locate a room-and-board situation where the landlord (or housemate) has experience in disabilities. Again, community agencies may be of assistance, or try colleges or university faculties in areas of human services (social work, nursing, rehabilitation). A student studying in these areas could be a perfect fit in this situation.

- Explore employment or volunteer programs that provide accommodations with the job. These could include building schools in third world countries with a charitable group, being a ranch hand on a farm, or serving as a live-in housekeeper!

- Keep them at home and anticipate caring for them, partners and, potentially, grandchildren. Grandbabies have been a real source of joy for some families. The more the merrier!

Like any parent, you are going to go through the natural stages of having an adult child move out. As nervous as you may feel, concentrate on the memories and try to focus on the new life that is ahead for all of you. Grief and loss may come into play again during this time, but it might just be smoothed over a bit when you realise that their old room is actually big enough to install a sauna!

Searching for biological parents

Adopted youth or adults may express an interest in contacting their biological parents at some point. Due to the established diagnosis of FASD, there are several possibilities to consider: (1) The biological parent(s) may be in recovery, (2) The biological parent(s) continue to struggle with substance abuse issues, (3) There may be other siblings that may or may not be alcohol-affected that your child did not know existed, and (4) The parent(s) may be since deceased. For any reunification, the unknowns are difficult to plan for and precautions are necessary to prepare your child and you for the outcome. It might turn out to be a very positive reunion where the birth parent(s) have dealt with their issues and could become an alternate support system to your child (given they accept the information regarding the medical diagnosis). Another possibility is that the substance abuse has worsened, and related problems such as financial instability, domestic violence, or criminal activities could be pervasive. There is also a chance that the biological mother may adamantly deny any use of alcohol in her pregnancy, further confusing your child. Conversely, she might be able to deal very appropriately with the psychological ramifications of your child's disability and act as a support. But there is a real possibility that your child will be gravely disappointed in the discovery; this coupled with the consequences of the disability makes it much harder to process such emotional issues. It might also shake out some unexpected emotions for you as well. In any case it is crucial that you explore the possibility of therapeutic support for your child and yourselves prior to and after venturing into the search, because you'll have to be prepared for anything.

Legal issues

As a society, when someone breaks the law, we usually want them punished and have things (liberties and/or reputation) "taken away" from them. Consequences such as monetary fines, community service hours, or incarceration were designed to deter people from committing illegal behaviours. The problem is that some patients simply don't respond to deterrence and punishment the way we want them to. Some don't realize that they have done anything wrong in the first place. Others have drastically miscalculated the costs versus rewards to the activity, especially when the variable of risk for detection has to be factored in. This deficiency in accurate computation is exactly why many youths are able to be talked into offending by "friends" or continue re-offending after being caught once. In some cases youth and adults may find incarceration quite comforting because there is strict routine: someone tells them when to get up and when to eat, and there are very few self-directed demands. As discussed earlier, it is not appropriate to hold a separate Court or segregated sentencing only for the alcohol-affected; many other offenders have a variety of central nervous system dysfunction (including being in the Intellectually Deficient range of functioning for other reasons).

A shift in how we think about the terms of punishment needs to occur because the entire premise is based on someone being able to learn from the negative experience and adjust accordingly. For those that require sentencing we need to accommodate the expectations so that they are obtainable. This may include supports such as other individuals ensuring that they get to and from the scheduled community service, such as helping at a Food Bank. Sentencing that addresses the particular offence would be considered the most beneficial. For example, a young man who has been repeatedly charged with physical and verbal assault all towards females could be directed to counselling with a trained therapist, with the goal to introduce sensitivity training at his developmental abilities and not chronological age. A mentor could be assigned that is responsible for modeling appropriate behaviour towards women and supervising him at community events. The focus of the intervention is designed to address the specificity of the crime. Repeated offences typically reflect that the level of supervision should be heightened and programming adjusted according to the individual's learning style and abilities. Ironically, **the number of conditions should be reduced and designed in such a way so that the patient is able to accomplish the set out conditions; written conditions are never a substitute for good supervision.** Contrast this with the sentencing theory of the "step principal," whereby each time one comes back to Court for the same offence the punishment increases. This practice has the potential for seemingly cruel and unusual punishments (which are disproportionate to the crime) for individuals who are "simply not getting the message."

Another core area of concern in the Courts has been the open discussion identifying the patient as "FAS." This has been done not only in front of the individual but also to an open Courtroom with lawyers, Court reporters, other young persons, parents, Social Workers, Probation Officers, and general public in attendance, most of them having nothing to do with the case. It is the writer's opinion that this is a clear violation of the patient's privacy regarding a medical disposition, not to mention the impact on his or her dignity. A young man shared a devastating experience where the judge asked him if he knew what it meant to be FAS. He responded, "Yeah, it means I'm retarded." He later faced teasing from other kids and a barrage of well-meaning individuals (including the judge) who attempted to explain his disability to him, which embarrassed and saddened him. He confided that he didn't like people talking negatively about his mother (who had recently recovered from alcoholism), as the two were beginning to rebuild their relationship. He felt defensive, depressed and angry. As stated earlier, we have two standards: one for FASD-affected individuals and one for those with other disabilities. Would it be considered appropriate for a lawyer or judge to ask individuals if they know what it means to be "intellectually deficient or have Down syndrome"? Would others approach the individual and attempt to explain the chromosomal implications and gestational periods of damage?

Now that the Courts are requesting assessments and diagnosis of potentially FASD-affected persons, this issue warrants further exploration. In Calgary, Alberta, Canada the **OBD** Triage Institute completes premedical screening assessments which are referred to as **OBD** (Organic Brain Dysfunction) Triage Assessments ©. They are intended to evaluate the possibility of many teratogens including genetic possibilities, virus, German Measles, x-rays, drugs, maternal nutrition, etc. The results of the **OBD**

Triage Assessment Reports indicate only whether there has been a positive or negative screen for potential teratogens, not exclusively alcohol. Other possibilities for handling this issue may be that all medical reports state clearly that this information is not be discussed in Court in front of the patient, and that all care and precautions are applied. Medical professionals are available to patients and their families, and should be exclusively responsible to explain to the youth (if appropriate) and families the ramifications of the diagnosis. As parents you are in a position to voice this concern to the medical teams and justice officials that may be involved with not only your child but others, in order to advocate for changes to the existing systems.

Many parents have disclosed their concerns about who will care for their adult child when they pass on. A legal Will and Testament could include a trust fund with monies to be released on a monthly basis and determine whether a family member, friend or a Public Guardian should be established well in advance to take over in the event of your death. It is never too early to plan for the inevitable. Put together a network and establish an "anchor" person or agency that will act as a homing device in the long term. By discussing these issues with your spouse and family and formulating a legal plan with your lawyer, you will have one less thing to worry about in the long term. That way everyone will know, including your adult child, what to expect.

The good news . . . they eventually level out!

The good news is that after years of observation it appears that this population are classically late bloomers and eventually tend to settle down (usually in their late twenties or early thirties). In many instances this success can be attributed to their finding a partner who suits them, takes on the finances and keeps them organized.

They eventually seem to find a place in life where they fit in comfortably. This can be anywhere from a full-time supportive residential placement, to living with a friend or partner, or on their own with the benefit of outside supports. Without those supports they are at a higher risk for victimization by others and for impulsive choices. Nonetheless, they'll still find their kind of happiness and occasionally turn up for dinner unannounced - count on it!

Persons diagnosed with FASD have a greater chance of ...

Physical abuse
Being sexually assaulted
Feelings of inadequacy
Low self-esteem
Physical anomalies
Familial dysfunction
Sibling maltreatment
Stress
Sleep disorders
Us making generalizations about them
Feelings of being unwanted
Numerous residential placements
Attachment problems
Unsuccessful academic performance
Feeling unintelligent
Frequently being misdiagnosed and misunderstood
Constant frustration
Chronic fatigue
Eating disorders
Finding it more difficult to enjoy relaxation
The necessity for medications
Numerous medical appointments
An unplanned pregnancy
Depression
An elevated risk for substance abuse
Easily victimized
Feeling embarrassed
Being led into prostitution or gang activities
Sporadic employment
Poor financial status
Losing things of value
Being incarcerated
Incurring consequences for things they may not understand
Short-term and tumultuous friendships
Confusion for why others are mad at them
Us giving up on them

AND an even greater chance of experiencing . . .

Being spontaneous
Making many friends in a lifetime
Having fun
Being courageous
Feeling uninhibited
Having a great memory for songs
Being persistent
Being an imaginative thinker
Having an unconventional career
Being athletic
Exhibiting kind-heartedness
Being able to fit in small places
Having many people care for them
Finding creativity in many places
Becoming a role model for someone else
Experiencing a new adventure every day
Having the opportunity to be parents
Making us laugh
Demonstrating resolve
Having nice teeth
Sticking to their guns
Not caring what others think
Having unusual talents
Not fearing fear
Excelling on a computer
Taking risks
Being a prolific writer
Showing generosity to those less fortunate
Never having to worry about being overweight
Being a social butterfly
Thinking outside of the box
Enjoying sensations
Becoming a great storyteller
Loving animals
Seeing what we don't see
Appreciating alone time
Knowing that we love them

Chapter Twelve

The Mothers we don't know

Fetal Alcohol Syndrome is the only form of brain injury where we identify someone to blame - the Mom. The identification of this historic phenomenon has created the need for therapeutic interventions to be curtailed *specifically* to the issues that are entwined in dealing with a mother who drank alcohol in her pregnancy, as well as for the person that was affected. Treatment must be offered free of judgment or blame, insinuation of fault, or subtle condemnation. In order to effect **prevention** and raise healthy children, we need to explore our true feelings regarding women who drink while pregnant. I suggest trying an exercise to compel you to identify how you really feel regarding this issue.

Exercise: You are out on a Saturday night with friends at a local lounge. You see a pregnant woman drinking - what would you do? During the process of this discussion, appraise your own use of alcohol and/or drugs. You may discover that your opinions are linked to your values.

Common Responses to the question:

"How do you know that she is actually pregnant?"

"It is the bartender's responsibility to cut her off."

"I would talk to her or her friends and give her information on FASD."

"I'd tell her that her baby is going to be brain damaged and that she should stop being so selfish."

A new perspective

Back in 1989, I did my first interview with a woman who was a recovered alcoholic and had five children. She suspected that at least three of them were affected. The assessment process includes very personal questions regarding social circumstances such as emotional, physical and sexual abuse, which she was readily willing to answer, saying, "I want to do what is best for my kids." She disclosed that when she was, she thinks, about five to six years of age, missionaries took her from her parents in the fall. By winter she missed her parents dreadfully and started making attempts to run away. As a preventative measure, her shoes were hidden, but she exclaimed: "I didn't care. I was going home." One night she started out running in the snow. She described how heavy it was on her legs and how she could hear the nuns "trying to start the old jalopy like the keystone cops," and she smiled. Then a strange calm came over her face as she quietly explained that they had caught her and the next thing she remembered was the "warmth on the back of my legs." She explained that this was from the blood running down her back from where she had been beaten with a tree switch. She still has the scars on her back, buttocks and legs today. As I sat astounded with admiration for her honesty and inner strength, she looked down at my papers and said: "I see the next question is about the sexual abuse; let's continue. That same night that I ran away, my nightgown was sticking to my legs (because of the bleeding), and the nun put me in the cold shower to wash off. In there she made me do the oral sex on her. She then took me to my room, and later the priest came in and did the same thing." She was six years old.

Thirteen years later, a physician's referral introduced me to a woman who lived in a very opulent home complete with housekeepers and gardeners. Her family was extremely wealthy and quite well known in the "Society" pages. She had recently completed her fourth stay at a private treatment centre for alcoholism and prescription medication abuse. In discussing her alcohol consumption she recalled on a typical day drinking a pitcher of martinis in an evening and sometimes needing a Bloody Mary in the morning to tide her over till afternoon. All three of her children required further medical evaluation for FASD. A week later, she called me requesting another meeting at her home. On the way there I was puzzled about the purpose of the session as she had been very precise as to the amounts of alcohol she drank while pregnant, and as to her health and obstetrical history. Upon my arrival she quickly shared, "I didn't tell you the truth when you were last here," and she started to cry. "I've never told anyone this, but my father would come into my room at night and get into bed with me. It hurt so much, and one time I remember blood on my pretty yellow sheets. I was so scared. I eventually told my mother when I was in grade two. She told me to stop this nonsense and that we would never do better than my dad and that we needed the money." Her best recollection is that the rape began when she was about five years old and continued until she was twenty-eight years old. She wanted paternity tests done, because she was concerned that her biological father might have fathered two of her children.

It is easy to be angry at someone you feel is responsible for your child's brain injury, in this case the biological mother. What we need to be mindful of in discussing such an emotionally charged subject is that children view themselves as 50 percent made from mom and 50 percent made from dad. In expressing distaste for their biological mothers we indirectly cause hurt and shame to the children, who see this criticism as a reflection of them. They internalize that they are also bad in some way but don't know why. Alcoholism is a disease, often hereditary, and kids need to know that their Mom did not drink on purpose because that's the truth. How many of us can say for sure that we didn't drink alcohol prior to realizing we were pregnant, or we did later and now are afraid to talk about it? In being privileged enough to have interviewed over 600 women to date, I have yet to meet a woman who intentionally drank in her pregnancy. It's just not the way it works.

It is crucial that we recognize the horrendous sexual, physical and emotional abuse of female children as **the** mitigating factor in the prevention of FASD. As the saying goes, "women drink to forget and men drink for courage," and that's how it starts. Prevention dollars must be directed to the abolishment of sexual, physical and emotional abuse, and to counselling for those that have already been victimized. The incorporation globally of FASD Education classes in junior and senior high schools must be made a social priority. FASD-affected individuals require specific prevention programs designed to accommodate their learning abilities, as well as social and hereditary histories, in order for them to understand how to stop the cycle for the next generation.

We need to talk to our boys to be sure to teach them how to really respect women, and let them know that they are also an intricate and vital part of prevention. For you men out there, put down that beer if your partner is expecting your baby, and give her a hug instead. The best method of prevention for future or high-risk pregnancies is to instil some kindness into a mom's day; show her we care and understand without hidden agendas or insinuated fault. Only then will women feel that they are able to reach out for help when addictions are in control of their lives and they are not.

Information is most influential, so tell someone who will tell someone else. I firmly believe that in time, and with the appropriate interventions, Fetal Alcohol Spectrum Disorders will be a thing of the past. By focusing on appreciating, respecting and supporting female children and women we can make it happen.

Chapter Thirteen

Families making it work

Hi, my name is Juanita and I am a single mom of five children: Matthew nineteen years old, Andy five, both adopted. I am also a foster mom to three daughters ages eight, twelve and thirteen. All my children are alcohol affected with the exception of my eight year old. Life in my home is chaotic, frantic at times, challenging and FUN.

My parenting is beyond the "norm." It is inventive, imaginative, creative and full of choices, and hardly ever does the same thing work twice. There are no easy answers. The one thing that always works and is a constant in my home is a sense of humour! Structure and routine keep us all in line and everyone fairly happy. I educate myself as much as possible, and I network with as many people as I can. I attend foster and adoptive support groups. I also receive advice, education and support from a FASD Parent Mentor.

Let me tell you about my boys. Matthew has been with me since birth. He was a preemie and with that came all of the usual complications. FASD didn't enter the picture until he was 16 years old. He was a happy boy, and there were no "problems" until he entered playschool. He was told he was hyper and failed to "pay attention" during circle time. A medical assessment indicated that Attention Deficit Hyperactivity Disorder was the diagnosis, and the referrals to special programs started. Matthew attended a Learning Centre for one year and that was the beginning. At this time I was told that he was developmentally delayed and would benefit by being placed in a small, structured class. He did incredibly well in this setting throughout grades one to six. Junior high school was a horrific experience for Matthew. This was the point in his life when he realised that he was different from the others. He stuck out like a sore thumb. He was bullied constantly and seen at the hospital Emergency Room on two occasions because of physical and verbal intimidation by his peers.

When Matthew reached 17, I began to worry about what would happen to him when he turned 18. As a foster parent, I was pretty sure that Matthew was alcohol affected, as FASD was prevalent in my home. The Children's Hospital team confirmed my concerns. When the doctor told him that he was alcohol-affected, his response was "That explains a lot" and that he was glad it had a name. Matthew was placed in a modified program, and although he struggled at first, he eventually found his footing. He was awesome. During this time it became apparent that Matthew struggled in math and reading and had difficulties retaining information. He would "zone out" when it became too much for him. He continues to do this as an adult. Senior high school was good for Matthew. He attended a modified program and once told me that he "fit in." In grades 10 and 11 he was on the Honour List. When he reached grade 12 his grades started to suffer and his self-esteem sunk lower and lower. His "friends" encouraged this, and they started to take advantage of him. The only good thing about it all is that I have a great relationship with my son and he would tell me everything. I sought out counselling for both of us, and it helped a great deal. He was so pleased when he graduated . . . me too!

Matthew will always struggle but with support will continue to thrive. He is a great artist - drawing and sketching is his life. He hopes to attend an art program or college. The other great love in Matthew's life is his brother, Andy.

Andy came to me as a sickly baby with lots of problems because he was drug affected at birth. He was in and out of the hospital for the first six months of his life. At three months of age, I was told he was HIV positive and might or might not live to his first birthday. It didn't stop Matthew and me from falling in love with him. He was a difficult baby to mother - he didn't sleep and wouldn't eat, and I couldn't soothe him. He didn't like to be touched, bright lights bothered him, and so did most noises, but I loved him anyway.

We celebrated his first birthday with a quiet bang.

He was still slowly growing, but the usual milestones were late in coming. He did not crawl, and there was no "baby talk," and he was still not sleeping through the night. Even now, at five years old, he doesn't sleep through the night.

We celebrated his second birthday with another quiet bang.

As a toddler, Andy was medically evaluated, and the diagnosis was that he was not only drug affected but alcohol affected. By then, I noticed he was forgetting words that he had already learned. He said "Momom" for the first time at two and a half and started walking. I was so happy, I cried. He was enrolled in the Children's Hospital school program, and with early intervention he was accepted into a specialized preschool.

The bangs got a little louder with birthdays three, four and five!

He is now in kindergarten and doing very well. It has been noted that he appears to have memory lapses as well as problems with word retrieval and "zoning out." Andy still becomes upset with too much light and noise. Andy has a lot of challenges ahead of him including his health. He has been hospitalised several times, and he manages to surprise us all with his will to survive despite the odds. Andy loves dinosaurs, PlayStation, games and making pictures for everyone.

My girls . . . well, that would take a whole book. They do have their challenges, but we have fun.

As I said at the beginning of this passage, humour is the thing that keeps us all going. I can laugh at just about anything, and I usually do. I have passed this on to ALL of my children . . . because if you can't laugh at yourself, you're in trouble. I get out once a week. I joined a bowling league; now that's something to laugh about! My children and I take respite from each other monthly for a weekend or so. My family helps quite a bit. Never think that you can do this on your own - you can't. My family supports all that I do even when they don't understand. All I have to do is ask. My friends make sure that I have an outlet away from everything, and man, do we laugh!

On a wing and a prayer we have made it this far. With a generous helping of love and humour we will continue to do so. I love them all dearly.

Juanita

My husband, Kim and I were blessed with three fabulous FASD children. At the time we adopted each of them, they were not FASD, or so we were told. There is Nick, age 18; Josh 14; and Lisanne, who's seven years old. In 1988, we adopted Nick who was just turning three. He was a lively, enthusiastic boy. We soon enrolled him in preschool. This went well because he had another lively boy to play with. Kindergarten was okay, but he always wanted to be touching other children. This stopped by grade one, but the attention problems began to be more noticeable. By the middle of grade two it was obvious that Nick had challenges. I questioned whether he might be FAS. Since there was no formal testing for FAS at that time and he did better in school with Ritalin, Nick was diagnosed with Attention Deficit Hyperactivity Disorder by grade three.

This was when we adopted Josh, who was 14 months old. He was a joy. His speech and motor skills were delayed, and he was also painfully shy. Josh finally spoke to his preschool teacher near the end of his second year there. School had been difficult for him because he has difficulty reading. Math makes sense to him, but reading does not. At the end of year two, we learned that Josh's sister was available for adoption. He was thrilled that his sister would be coming to live with us . . . that is, until he felt that she was getting all the attention.

Lisanne was nearly two years old when she came to live with us. She was adorable. She was also speech delayed but soon caught up. Lisanne's biggest problem in school is keeping on task. Time is of no consequence to her. The word "hurry" will bring her to a grinding halt. Preschool was not a problem for her. She loves crafts and playtime.

Meanwhile Nick was doing okay. He was going to school because that is where his friends were. He was and is a very sociable person. He never had behavioural problems at school.

But Josh started refusing to go to school some days. It started at the end of grade four. He would hide under his bed or go into a fetal position. We hoped that he would get over whatever mood he was in. He initially attended at the beginning of grade five, but the refusals soon came. Through the school we had the specialized programs, and Josh was seeing a psychologist through Children's Mental Health. He spent a month in a residential school program housed at the Children's Hospital. Josh completed a medication (Ritalin) trial while in hospital. It helped with the attention problems but did nothing to address the attendance refusals.

In the spring of 2001, Kim and I had come to the end of our patience. Josh had tunnelled through a wall in his closet. He was missing more than one day of school a week. In desperation, I called the Crisis Line. Fortunately, an FASD specialist was on the other end. After I ranted for a while, he asked me some questions. Then he asked if it was possible that Josh was alcohol affected. I said, "No," then "I don't know." He came over and spoke to Kim and me, then went to talk to Josh . . . under his bed. This led us to finally having all three children medically evaluated. This was difficult for us. We went from having one ADD child and two typical children to having three FASD children. It did, however, help explain some of the struggles that our family was having. Now what?

I called Post-Adoption Support Services for some help. Lisanne was fortunate to be diagnosed during Kindergarten. She got a good start with the well-supported programming there. She is now in grade two at our local elementary school, and she has a part-time aide. She can read well, and so far is not having problems with math. Her social skills with peers are fine. I talk to her teacher often and keep on top of any concerns. An early diagnosis will help us monitor Lisanne better and more closely.

Josh and I dealt with the Attendance Board with the Board of Education for about two years. Although often late, he does not miss many days anymore. Since his diagnosis, Josh has had a part-time aide in the classroom. I was concerned that he would not accept his first aide in grade seven, but it has gone well for the past two years. Josh has also seen a counsellor every second week, and he is making steady improvement, not only in school attendance, but also in other parts of his life. Josh has always had a small core of friends whom he went to preschool and Beavers with. He now has another small group of friends at his junior high school . . . some of them share the same aide with him. Josh is planning to be a professional baseball player when he grows up. I keep trying to convince him that baseball players have to get out of bed early for practices, so he should start practicing getting up on time now.

This brings me to Nick. School was always a challenge for him although he has an average I.Q. I would help him do his homework, but he would forget to hand it in. I spent a week in his classroom throughout elementary school to keep him on track. Junior high school was more challenging. His only saving grace was that his teachers liked him. He is friendly, outgoing, and means well, but he cannot follow through on completing anything.

High school did not go well. He did well in automotives and building services classes rather than written assignments. But as he puts it, I ruined his life. He did not get to go to the same high school as his friends. However, he met new friends who showed him how to skip school. He did complete grade 10. Grade 11 was a disaster. Not only was he skipping school, but he was smoking marijuana. He just didn't care about school. We called the Crisis Line. Nick spent a few days in a short-term Residential Stabilization Program. He said that he wanted to be at the same school as his friends. The staff contacted the vice principal, and Nick was told to finish the year and they would see how his grades were when considering a change of schools. A few days later, Nick got a letter from the vice principal saying that Nick was not likely to be welcome there. He started staying out late or just not coming home. He was agitated, obnoxious at home, taking things that didn't belong to him and punching holes in the wall. He was getting violent because of his frustration. It was at this point that Nick was diagnosed with FASD.

We tried to get Nick to finish the school year, but when it was obvious that he wouldn't, we offered to pull him out and try again in September. The school staff got him a job. It paid 10 dollars an hour; he worked there for about a month and then stopped going. He wouldn't even go in to quit the job. He didn't know why he wouldn't go back to work. Nick spent the summer thinking about getting a job. He had his first legal problem. He was caught sitting in a car with a girl. The buses probably weren't running. This girl wanted to go to downtown, so she suggested they steal a car. Nick did not know how to drive or steal a car. He has since figured out how to drive and has stolen our car a few times. In September, Nick tried school again. It did not work. He spent several nights at a Shelter. He wasn't doing anything. We were feeling helpless.

I called Child Welfare for help. Nick spent seven months in a Supported Independent Living (SIL) Placement. He did not get a consistent Youth Worker. This was very confusing for Nick. He started going missing. The placement broke down; his bed was closed with only one day's notice, so he had to come home again. His Child Welfare Worker told him that he would have to live at a shelter until she could secure another placement. He would come home every night, and we would drive him there. He started coming home later and later until he lost his bed at the Shelter. He was afraid to be downtown. Nick has had several legal problems usually dealing with a car - not his, or breach of curfew, school attendance, or other probation obligations. Time has run out.

Last Christmas day, Nick turned 18 and is no longer Child Welfare's problem. I had put in the paperwork for the Assured Income for the Severely Handicapped (AISH) and Persons with Developmental Disabilities (PDD) Programs. Nick recently qualified for AISH, thank goodness. Now he is finding out the hard way that this will not be enough money to keep him in the lifestyle in which he would like to live. But he still does not understand that he will need a job to make money for all the extras like cigarettes or CD's, or to take his girlfriend on a date. Although Nick does not qualify for the PDD Program (his I.Q. is too high), he was chosen as one of the lucky test subjects for a new Strive Project designed to attend to persons like Nick who, although they do not qualify, still require support services. He will be trying a new SIL placement again. We will hold our breath and pray.

The biggest challenge that Nick faces is "waiting." He was built for action and/or reaction. Waiting, while the wheels of the system turn, is painful and nearly impossible for him. The longer the waiting period, the more likely that Nick will disappear for a while or get into trouble. It is difficult for his parents to keep enthusiastic about an upcoming program when we cannot tell him when it will start.

The FASD Society Parent Support Group has been my lifesaver and is my lifeline to sanity. Raising FASD children can be very hard on a marital relationship. I have a very caring, kind, supportive and wonderful husband. When one of us runs out of energy, the other is always there to carry on. As a poster in our home states, "Every day is a new adventure." We have had to adjust our hopes and plans for the future. I am reluctantly giving up my FASD Parent Peer Mentor job because my children are demanding more of my time again. My husband's job has been impacted by lost opportunities because he is always too busy with home situations. Kim and I do go to the theatre together. We also have very supportive families and friends.

Each of my FASD children is affected differently. Along with the varying disabilities that my children are coping with, they have strengths that see them through. They try so very hard to get through each day. It is all the small successes that other parents take for granted that give me strength to keep advocating for my children. They will need outside help, probably for the rest of their lives. I hope that my children, with a little help and understanding, will be able to make some kind of contribution to the world around them. With a little bit of luck and by the grace of God, we will survive.

Melanie

My story will follow the timeline of my son's life, outlining the good times, what was working, the bad times and what wasn't working. Please excuse me if my emotions show.

My son has basically all the protective factors: stable, nurturing family his entire life, early diagnosis, never experienced violence towards himself. He has a low-normal IQ (80ish) and presents with autistic and bipolar-like tendencies. This means that, unlike many adolescents with FASD, he is not a social butterfly. Although this means that he is terribly lonely, we believe it helps protect him, because he is not invited to parties or out to a variety of locations with people we don't know. He observes his Dad who has no male friends to socialize with, just colleagues he's friendly with. Dad is happy with his wife and kids; my son believes that if only he could find a girlfriend, he would be as content as his father. Thus, at 15, he is on a constant search for the girl that will transform his life.

As far as friends go, he does have two. One has Asperger's syndrome (form of autism) and the other has been diagnosed bipolar with probable FASD. He has no high-functioning, protective "good" friends. So how did we get from zero to 15? Well, he was a difficult baby. Looking back we were fortunate to have had in-home childcare and did not need to use a daycare system. He attended a community preschool program where his teacher advised us to hold him back a year, which we did. His elementary years were spent in the same school as the preschool, reducing his transitions from programs.

Later on, as a result of his violent tendencies, I decided to do everything in my power to see Gareth was never unsupervised or able to attack children. I began to walk with him, not only to and from school, but also directly to and from his classroom every morning, noon and night.

Many teachers and parents anxiously approached me to tell me of each new incident they had witnessed or heard about. At the start of grade six he had no aide and he continued threatening teachers, and then eventually, and I hate to say this but, THANK YOU, GOD - he slugged his teacher. She got the Teacher's Association onside and forced the school board to find a different placement for him. This was my turning point and what I believe all families face at sometime.

Gareth was growing older, entering adolescence, and was becoming more violent. I had a younger daughter whom I needed to protect. I was a humiliated, terrified, basket case. I picked up the phone to call Social Services to say "come and get him - I cannot do this anymore." As I started to dial, I quite literally heard a voice say, "No one can do a better job with this boy than you can. Your love will keep you going where others will give up." So I hung up and decided "okay, what now?" I developed a new objective - I would do the best I could, I would try to prevent the worst, and I would talk openly to anyone who would listen about the horrors of prenatal alcohol exposure.

As Gareth's behaviour deteriorated, many people surprised me. Some who I had thought would stand by me abandoned us. Others who had been casual friends and neighbours stepped forward and offered heart-warming, life saving support. Although the rejections hurt deeply, I learned to lean on those offered support. Eventually I learned to turn a blind eye to the rejections and fears of others and focus on my family and my child's needs.

My goals for Gareth became to

- Keep him alive

- Ensure that he is fed, clothed, housed ideally at home

- Keep him healthy, off street drugs and alcohol

- Keep him out of jail

- Prevent parenthood

I started to use some tools I already had and got some new ones:

My husband is an extremely supportive, involved man, so I began to lean on him more.

I have some wonderful friends, and I began to find out which ones would support me in the ways I needed.

I became involved in a FASD Parent Support Group.

I read everything I could find about FASD.

I went to my doctor to get help for my stress levels.

I got Caller I.D. installed on my phone so I could decide if I needed a few minutes to prepare myself, should familiar phone numbers ring.

I got a cell phone so I could leave the house yet still be accessible to school staff and babysitters.

I started getting regular massages.

I live with my Fears.

I fear he'll hurt someone and I say to myself . . . Well, he's little, the chances are unlikely.

I fear he'll get hurt and I say to myself: few people are fighters; keep him out of bars-the odds are on his side.

I fear he'll live with me forever, and I say to myself: I won't live forever.

I fear I'll have to support him forever, and I say to myself: Okay, so get on with it.

I used the equity in my house to buy a second house nearby on a bus route, near groceries, small bar, etc. I'm renting it currently to get it partially paid for.

My will differentiates between my son and daughter. I have provided for his share of our estate to be spread over his anticipated lifetime with exclusions for such things as jail time. I have increased life insurance to provide increased long-term funding.

And I'm on the lookout for a high functioning woman wanting a secure home with a sweet but moody man.

In the meantime, what strategies am I using? Here are a few:

I keep **perspective** by reciting my goals for parenting him over and over.

I have given him a **routine** - he has a written job list for his morning tasks. Sometimes he reads it, and sometimes he needs me to. (My husband doesn't use a written list for evening jobs and they fight more. Is it the male dynamic? Is it that they're both tired? Is it the lack of a list? . . . I don't know but IT IS NOT MY PROBLEM.)

I try to **let it go** - be it Nintendo, computer games, pornography; as long as he grudgingly leaves them when he's called, they're okay with me.

I hope to keep him in **school** for as long as possible in a small class, minimize academic stress, provide a "flight" option to reduce the "fight" instinct, and advocate, advocate, advocate.

I keep my tongue quiet about his infuriating and weird friends. Some mother will do the same for me, I hope. As often as possible, I have his friends at our home where there is supervision.

I provide safety netting, such as a cell phone.

I provide limits like permission to go to the LOCAL mall but not other malls, bus only to specific destination and not all over the city, and some time alone at home to allow him to practice some emerging adult skills.

And the most controversial of all, I try to keep his stress at a minimum by saying **yes** as often as possible and saying **not today** whenever I can't say yes.

I want to conclude by reminding you of my Goals for him and what I hope will be **your** starting goals for those adolescents affected by FASD who are in your lives:

Keep them alive
Ensure they are fed, clothed, housed - ideally at home
Keep them healthy, off drugs and alcohol
Keep them out of jail
Prevent parenthood

For this, I thank you.

Berna

Hello, my name is Peggy. I am a nurse, a FASD Parent Mentor and a mother of a child with FASD. My son is 23 years old. We made it through his teenage years. He is employed, has a girlfriend and still lives at home. We will be looking for a place for him to live soon because he has been stable for the past six months. By stable I mean he is, in most part, in control of his behaviour and reactions to different things. This is due to exposure to many and repeated experiences with support close by. There are a lot of things that he doesn't understand about society and things he just will never get even when exposed to them. He will need the support of someone looking out for him at a "not so far" distance the rest of his life. He can function in society with support.

I have no great words of wisdom, nor do I have a no-fail plan. What I would like to share with you is a conversation I had with my son not too long ago. I asked him about his teenage years and what he remembers and what he would change if he had the opportunity. First, he told me that he wished he could be like everyone else. He didn't want to be different. He said he never knew what was going on most of the time around him. Everyone else knew but he didn't. Secondly, he said he wanted to have one good friend. Not someone who said they would be his friend and then a few days later decided to call him names or beat him up. Not only that, kids he didn't even know would pick on him or want to beat him up. He never knew why. I guess the other kids would start rumours. He said to this day he doesn't know what he did to cause this. Looking back, he said, "I would do the dumbest things to fit in, even though I never fit in. I would do or say anything to have a friend. If these so-called friends would ask me to do dumb things, I did them. I wouldn't listen to someone who actually cared for me; that's how badly I wanted a friend. For the most part I was either alone or very lonely. That was really hard growing up, to have no one I could talk to that was the same age. Adults wouldn't call me names because they knew better. I got along better with the adults than I did the kids. Now I'm an adult and I can see the dumb things I did to fit in. The only thing I did was get myself into a lot of trouble, and I still didn't have a friend."

Looking back on those teenage years, I recognize it was the most difficult time for him, our family and me. While he was in elementary school, things were bad enough, but now he was in junior high school. At age 13, I started to explain to him about FASD after he came home again very frustrated, calling himself stupid far too many times. Academically, he was at his limit. He went through a grieving period for about three years where he denied it, blamed his mother, got angry; he would cry and then he would start all over again. He went through a period of self-mutilation. He hated himself for being the way he was. He didn't have any friends, and trying to make new friends just got him into trouble with the teachers and the law. At least he now knew what it was he was dealing with, and it was not anything he was or wasn't doing. He didn't like it one bit. With support he did come to terms with it in his own time. Not everyone is the same, and we all have weaknesses and disabilities in certain areas. The problem is accepting them and getting on with what is important - living. He now tells people he can't do math very well, instead of pretending that he can. It's okay to ask questions when you don't understand. It's dumb not to.

Most children like to do well and don't intentionally set out to ruin everyone's day. Things just tend to go there naturally when someone lives with FASD. For one moment imagine yourself in the place of a Child diagnosed with FASD and what he or she must be going through, especially when the world doesn't seem to make much sense. I too would be very frustrated and angry most of the time with people asking me to do things or give them an answer when I still haven't figured out what the question is. Even when they ask me again what the question is - I still don't know.

As a parent I can only say we did it one day at a time.

- Medication did help.

- Having a support person to talk to makes it not so crazy.

- Do things at your child's level and ability, not where everyone else thinks he or she should be.

- Remember, these children will say or do anything to get what they want or to stay out of trouble. Tell your children, as they get older, that they need to be in control of themselves or someone else will be. As the parent you can manage the situation, but you need the young adult to be in control.

- These children need to be rewarded even for the smallest thing. You can't compliment them enough.

- Try to "positive parent." Your child will always have someone else in society to tell him or her how stupid he or she is. It shouldn't be from you. Children need your support. Any child does better knowing he or she is loved and supported. Take that away and any child will not do as well.

I didn't even like my son as a teenager. As an adult, though, he is funny, kind and very likable. It is a long haul, but well worth it. I'm glad we made it.

Peggy

I was born in 1978 and was adopted at the age of three. I was diagnosed with FASD at a young age. I have had many struggles throughout my lifetime with family, friends, education and finding myself. Throughout my adolescence I struggled with addictions and self-doubt.

Each and every person learns differently. The following strategy is one that I have found to be helpful in discovering my personal learning style. Math, Social, Science, English are the four core subjects taught to us throughout school. Theses subjects provide us with great knowledge that we cannot understand unless we are taught them. Throughout my school years I struggled with learning techniques used by teachers. I wasn't able to sit and read something then find the answer and present it on paper. It sounded easy enough, but for me it was so much more complicated. I needed to feel, see and hear the problem. When we were little kids teachers and parents would use bocks to help us do math. This was a great way to learn because you could see the number of blocks in front of you. Then you could take away or add more. If you had four blue blocks and took two away, you could see with your eyes and touch with your hands and then know in your mind that there are only two left. Though I was challenged with core subjects I did well in gym and drama. This was because I was active and doing things hands on. I was able to see the results in front of me as I did the work. If I shot the ball and missed the net, I could see what I needed to change but if I were to read the techniques of shooting a ball I couldn't put the words into actions. I could not always remember the steps to solve a math problem.

One of the skills that I have developed to help me with work and school is using repetition. Currently one of the jobs I do is run kids birthday parties. When I have a booking for a party I receive a receipt with the child's name, age and the activity they want. I have a copy of the receipt at work, then one at home. I write the booking in my personal notebook as well as my day timer and on my calendar. Then I highlight it all. I do this repetitive routine with every booking because it helps me to remember my schedule.

By far the best learning technique I have found is to embrace my challenges as learning opportunities. I have come to realize that I need to challenge myself with an understanding of failure, not a fear of it. When I decided to move out on my own, I was afraid that I would not be able to make it. This fear came from people around me believing that I could not make it and also the fact that I had not done it up to that point. I realized that sometimes I would have hard decisions to make. However, I wanted to experience independence and responsibilities and the drive to achieve this became larger than the fear. My parents have always been there for me no matter what. After many trials and tribulations I came to realize that I needed to take a chance and believe in myself. I felt that I had something special to offer and turned my struggles into strengths. I now travel around and share my life story of living with FASD. I do this in hope that people can see we all have struggles to overcome but with positive supports and belief that anyone can reach their goals and find their smile.

Myles

Things to know and understand about my child . . . from a birth father:

- Be mad at what happened to cause FASD, not the person who gave birth.

- Consider whether giving too much information will cause unnecessary concern that results in discriminatory actions toward the child with FASD.

- Remember to show understanding and forgiveness so the child does not lose face.

- Acknowledge the child's feelings.

- A child who sees an angry adult will stay defiant.

- Remember that the things a child has done were impulsive.

- It is hard on a child to have many caregivers.

- Don't say, "I am the adult; you listen to me because I know more." This assaults the child's self-esteem and opens the door to vengeful acts.

- To be a friend to my child, introduce yourself, say what your role is and find out what he likes. This will develop respect.

- Validate that the child has a role in the relationship - do it before the child forgets.

- Learn to forgive because the best thing you can do to understand how the child feels usually turns out to be an educated guess.

- It is not always easy to forgive, but it is important.

The longer a bad feeling is allowed to fester, the more emotional the outcome.

- As adults we should be able to empathize with children. Remember to remove the child from the deed.

- Discipline in a way that is relevant to the behaviour and is immediate.

- Always remember to try to help the child keep his dignity. Offer choices, but not too many - no more than two choices at a time so as not to overwhelm the child.

- Hear what the child has to say.

- The child may lie sometimes, so take time and remain calm. The truth is usually what you suspect. Remember this is related to the disability.

- If the problem occurred more than two hours ago, evaluate whether to pursue the incident because these children may have already forgotten what happened. At the very least, their memory may have changed to the truth created in their own mind.

- Protect your property in a way that is respectful. Be clear on the rules, keep locks on doors; you may even need a safe that can hold knives, medications and valuables of all sorts.

- Schools have to protect our children and others. Children are often overwhelmed with their emotions, and school is a place where it can be expressed. Other kids can sometimes really upset our kids. The frustration of not catching on can also cause trouble. If someone at the school lets them know he or she cares, it can help a lot.

- Put some fun into the child's day because this helps build a relationship for families.

- In the middle of a crisis, remember to let children know that you love them, but don't like what they did.

- Lies can come in many forms, sometimes because the child is afraid of more discipline. Lies can become a tool for survival. Children will often tell adults what they want to hear and not the truth. Ask the child to repeat *his or her understanding* of what you said.

- Search for the truth in a non-condemning way.

- Children present with many challenges while struggling everyday to do their best.

- Strengths need to be emphasized over weaknesses.

- Validating strength builds a more positive relationship.

- Believe in your child!

Dean

If you are thinking of adopting . . .

The intent of publishing this book was as much for parents that are considering adopting a child as it was for those already parenting in any capacity. As you know by now, there is a vast range of abilities within FASD, and as Forest Gump once said, "Life is box of chocolates. You never know what you're going to get." This is true for biological and adoptive parents alike. Nonetheless, you need to be informed about not just the delight a child can bring to your life, but the potential challenges as well. Most of all, you need to take time to evaluate, based on what you have read, heard or talked about with other parents, whether you are the type of person who is willing and able to be realistic about the various issues of this disability. If you can, please do this before you start visits with a child, not after - and don't rush. If it doesn't feel right, don't do it. Obtain and insist on as much information as possible including health history, medical diagnosis, cognitive testing, social history and potential mental health issues, genetic or hereditary factors. Explore shared-care possibilities and long-term supports for you and that special someone. Consider whether you are going to be the best fit for that particular child, and if not, know that you made a good decision in *their* best interest, not just yours.

Chapter Fourteen

Our kind of success

. . . is just a matter of a positive mindset. As you will see with these families, they have discovered the secret of finding the silver lining within the clouds!

Example 1: Relationship skills demand more sophistication in the teen years, and adolescence becomes an extremely emotional time for any youth. For those young persons with processing problems it can be even more complicated. One of the most ingenious teaching methods comes from a family with six teenagers. I know what you're thinking - they should be nominated for Sainthood or undergo psychiatric evaluation. In their busy home Friday nights have been designated "movie night." Instead of watching a store bought video - they make one. They rotate every week where one person gets to choose what type of take-out food they will have for dinner, and one gets to choose what the movie will be about. They have a "movie titles jar" which everyone contributes to that describes a social situation such as "Asking someone out for a date," or "A guy at the bus stop asks you if you want to buy some dope - what do you do?" ("Mom is getting on my nerves about cleaning" is my personal favourite.) The "director" sets up the video camera, all of the actors are assigned, and there is a costume designer and makeup artist. After the "shoot," they make some popcorn and watch their creation, while the laughter is at a roar. Trust me, Dad dollied up as Mom was an academy award calibre performance. On the occasional night when they are too tired or stressed, the assigned person gets to choose one of the existing movies that they have not viewed in a while; again, the hilarity is abundant. What they have achieved in this family are a number of things: predictability, structure, involving children in making choices, but mostly teaching social skills in a fun and creative way. Including the kids in the process enhances their chances of remembering what to do if and when the situation arises. The movies are always available for repeated viewing if they need a refresher for potentially problematic social interactions. For these parents, their originality has proved not only effective but also truly inspirational.

Example 2: Eating together as a family can be a wonderful daily ritual. It can also be the noisiest, most rambunctious, "I said sit in your chair, stop kicking the table and your brother" hair-raising experience going. The good news for the weight conscious is that you'll probably lose pounds because (a) you never actually eat an entire meal, (b) you burn off a fair amount of calories chasing kids around a table, and (c) expend even more calories pulling off one sister in her strangulation attempt. The bad news is that you may have to consider amending your meal traditions. An example of this is from a couple that were both raised with a family mealtime tradition. To them it is a sign of respect for each other (they have five children) that they all come together to discuss their day or important family news, and to be thankful for family and food. When they adopted Jack at six years of age, the celebration quickly came to a grinding halt. He was unable to sit still long enough to blink and is completely distractible, so conversations with him at this hour were, well, strained. It took him approximately one and a half hours to actually eat his food. He also earned the nickname "crash" because he tends to knock over everything he reaches for. Not fun, especially for Jack who usually ended up crying from frustration.

In examining Jack's profile with the family we realized that because of his hyperactivity component, even with medication, he still has to swing his legs and fidget. His distractibility is elevated due to not only the number of people, plates, cutlery and discussions, but the overall noise level, to which he has a particular sensitivity. He has very poor hand-eye coordination that makes it extremely difficult to execute motions such as reaching and grabbing with many items on the table. All these issues are directly related to his central nervous system dysfunction; in appreciating this the family sat down with Jack and asked him what he thought would be better for him. He came up with a doozie: "I want to eat by myself." Horrors. Isolate him? Not include him as a family member? Teach him to be disrespectful? After much soul searching, what we agreed on was to really listen to his idea. Now Jack eats separately from the family with a rotating family member earlier than when the entire family eats. Then he has "me-time": when the family is eating, he can do an activity in his room that is time-limited (they use a timer), or he can choose to watch television for half an hour in his parent's room. To him the latter is a treat because they have a big fluffy bed where he can lie down if he chooses and begin the evening process of winding down. On Sundays they all eat together so that Jack has intermittent practice at eating with others, and everyone seems to have more patience. It works for him and his family, and in making this change they have eliminated an insurmountable stress from their daily living. Giving up their predetermined customs and turning the conventional into unconventional is what made them tremendously successful.

Example 3: The one thing about having kids that require a little more energy is that they inspire great ideas, for instance, with Hal and his son Luke. Like many children, Luke has little to no awareness that he is standing way too close to people. This has made him most unpopular with a gaggle of grade six girls, with the exception of one that is now proposing marriage. His father devised an ingenious strategy to remind Luke of acceptable social distance. On a coffee visit with the family, Hal reminded me that he and Luke were die-hard Calgary Flames hockey fans (much like myself). During this conversation of bets, Hal smiled at Luke and said, "Why don't you show Liz your new cap?" Running excitedly to his room, Luke returned with a contraption I would not soon forget - an official Calgary Flames hockey cap with a set of plastic rods attached from the hat to a hula-hoop in coordinating colours. Luke gingerly walked over to me with his apparatus and said, "Liz, we are now the appropriate distance apart!" Now, make no mistake. Hal doesn't send Luke to school with this ingenious device, but it has proved to be an effective reminder for Luke to "see" the distance that he is not otherwise capable of determining. Proud as punch of his accomplishment, his dad looked at me and said, "You know, someday, all he'll need is the cap."

Example 4: A young teenage girl responding to her medical diagnosis and explanation of her physical anomaly of diminished facial creases: "So in other words, I'll look young forever and never need a facelift!"

Example 5: A shy teenage girl struggling in her physical education class went home to her mother and said, "I wish that I could be part of the team, but all I'm really good at is sewing." Thinking hard about her daughter's talent, the mother suggested that she sew a mascot costume for her school's athletic department. Thrilled at the opportunity, the girl talked to the coach who offered to pay for the materials and agreed to give her credit for the course. She stitched together the most fabulous costume using her own body for size. When she had completed the finished product she put it on, turned on some music, and danced around the house to the applause of her family. She is now one of the best team mascots in the business and has won awards for her performances.

Example 6: In discussing his primordial growth disturbance (even without increased calories he will continue to be underweight and small for his chronological age), an 11 year old turned to his folks and concluded, "Gee, that means I would be a great jockey - can I get a horse?" They did, and now he rides on the adult circuit.

Example 7: My dear friend Ray was 34 years of age when he was finally diagnosed with FASD. As a teenager he lived on the street, had experienced incarceration, became addicted to alcohol, and by 22 had unexpectedly fathered a child. He has lost thousands of dollars by repeatedly forgetting on the bus his coat containing his cashed pay check, or shelling out a good portion of his hard-earned money to those that he thought needed it more, and he was continually being evicted because of these circumstances. When I first met Ray he was singing a tribute at his mother's 50th birthday. You could have heard a pin drop in the community centre holding about 100 people. Later, in discussing his talent, Ray revealed that he knows the words to almost every song ever written. He might not be great with his tax return, but Ray has been a most sought after Deejay and Karaoke man in town. His success was achieved by following his instinct and a dream, but this is not the end of the story. As I was bragging about town regarding his fantastic accomplishment, my husband was doing Ray's taxes. Ray had decided to take financial responsibility for his son and wanted to eventually buy a home. They met one afternoon to exchange information, and my husband returned home and said, "Ray gave this to me, and I think you need to read it." It was the first chapters of his book about his life. As I lay sprawled on my sofa, I welled up with tears. It was profound. It was well written and heart wrenching. It needed no editing, and then it occurred to me. I was so focused on Ray's abilities in music that I had stopped looking for more of his strengths. I am a firm believer that you learn something new every day, and on that day I learned that just because someone has a label you should never cut him or her short. The fact was that I was so grateful to find one big aptitude to make him successful I stopped looking for others. Don't make my mistake. Keep looking. The results will be a pleasant surprise.

Chapter Fifteen

Laughter really is the best medicine

I read somewhere that those who laugh, last. As parents of children with disabilities, some of us might seem almost afraid to see the humour in some of the hysterical things that they do. **All** kids are funny in some way, and looking for it could bring out the best stress buster of all. Seek it out in them and yourself, and be ready for a good laugh. Laughter really is the best medicine!

Chuckle 1: At a repeat home visit with an aunt of two teenaged boys, we were going over some of the discussion from the prior visit regarding learning from experience. "I have a great example this week," she exclaimed. "As I walked past the boys' room I noticed that their beds were made and I had not even asked them to." She then went on to say that she called them upstairs into the bedroom, and having somewhat of a flair for the dramatic, she slapped her hand over her heart and said, "I think I'm having a heart attack! You actually made your beds without me asking!" She wound up her grand finale with a spin and plopped onto the bed still clutching her chest. As she lay there for a few seconds, she noticed that the room was incredibly quiet. "When I looked up, the two of them had eyes as big as plates!" Never to miss an educational opportunity, I smugly inquired, "So what did you learn from that experience, Betty?" "I'll tell you what I learned," she fired back. "If I ever have a heart attack I'm sure to die because those two kids ain't gonna call 911!"

Chuckle 2: Boy: "Mom, what's the name of my baseball team?" Mom: "The Chiefs." Boy: "Oh yeah, I can't get that out of my head!"

Chuckle 3: On her regular outings with her four-year-old grandchild, Grandma Paulette would be sure to keep Kleenex in her pocket in case of little sniffles. Her granddaughter had a field trip to the zoo the next day, which the Grandmother could not attend. In anticipation of the outdoor excursion, the Grandma tucked a couple of tissues in her granddaughter's coat so she would be well equipped. The next morning, as she was getting ready to leave, her granddaughter found the tissues in her pocket. Surprised, she evaluated her findings. "Look, Mom, Grandma must have borrowed my jacket!"

Chuckle 4: A boy and his father were attending the first meeting of the little-league baseball team. In the locker room, the coach, with a foot on the bench and looking very official, announced: "Men, you are all going to need special protection, so you have to wear a cup." "See, dad," the boy said with some trepidation. "If I hadn't broken that one in the kitchen last week, we wouldn't have to buy one!"

Chuckle 5: An adorable ten-year old girl came home from Sunday school with a passage she was to recite. "I can't read this!" she spouted. Always at the ready to help and sensitive to her daughter's needs, her mother reassured her, "Of course you can! Read it out loud; let's give it a try." Reluctantly, she screwed up her face and began, "I . . . will . . . not. . . I can't, I can't read this!" Calmly her mother hugged her and encouraged her to attempt it again. With a big sigh, she forced out, "I - will - not - lie. See! I told you I can't read it - I lie all the time!"

Chuckle 6: Eight-year-old David and his parents were standing in line waiting to be seated at a restaurant. The pretty blonde hostess cheerfully showed them to their table, and when handing David his menu the hostess flirtatiously joked: "Hey, you're kind of cute! Why don't we go out sometime to a movie?" Several minutes later, his mother noticed that David was unusually quiet with a very worried look on his face. "What's the matter, David?" she enquired. "Well, I don't know how she thinks we can go out to the movies when I don't even know how to drive!"

Chuckle 7: Accompanied by her father, Janet was practicing her newly honed driving skills in winter weather conditions. They went to an empty parking lot to practice stopping the car on ice. Dad was most impressed by her keen sense of caution and following through with his directions. On the way home they encountered a big snowy hill, and sure enough the vehicle got stuck on the ice. Staying calm, Dad began giving Janet step-by-step directions on how he would rock the car and for her to ease into the gas peddle. Eventually, the car started up the hill, and Dad continued to holler, "Keep going," which she did, until she got home. Dad, still at the bottom of the hill, was left to walk home.

Chuckle 8: One Sunday Tyler asked his mother if he could go to church with his friend, as he had never been. Upon his return his mother asked him how he enjoyed it. "It was fun, but I couldn't figure out where Ed was." "Who is Ed?" his mother inquired. "You know - God!" he insisted. "Why do you think God's name is Ed?" asked his confused mother. "Because, MOM, the minister said, 'Hallo Ed - be thy name!'"

Chuckle 9: A couple frequently had lively in-car discussions regarding the husband's driving speed. Their daughter Lisa was regularly seeing a speech therapist, who was working on her stringing three to four words together in a row like "I want milk, please." One day, Lisa and her father were alone in the car on their way to her appointment. As he rounded a sharp corner, he heard a small voice from the booster seat in the back clearly pronounce: "Judas Priest, Phil, slow down!"

In closing

A message to my colleagues

The identification of this medical disposition has been responsible for developing new areas of therapeutic interventions for all caregivers, affected youth and adults, birth moms and dads, as well as adoptive and foster parents. Therapists can become weary, particularly if their practice specializes in assisting families affected by FASD, because the issues often seem never ending - and for many that's the reality. Families may tend to be elated that you are the first therapist that they have encountered that truly understands their child's disability and their constant frustration. They will likely be sporadic visitors to your practice over the years, as opposed to a short-term therapeutic intervention. A short-term model of treatment is not going to be a fix for their problems. Therapists that venture into their world need to be cautious and not become pathologised within the disability's dysfunction. Be aware that supervision and/or colleague support need to be available on a regular basis because, like parents, you're going to be frustrated at times. It is not uncommon for families to rely heavily on a helping professional that has given them a light at the end of the tunnel. These families typically have much more strength and tenacity than they or sometimes we realize. The biggest lesson I have learned is to shut my big mouth and just listen. Most times all they need to keep them going is reassurance that they are doing a great job, because they are and they don't hear that nearly enough. Take time to rejuvenate yourself and maintain the energy that you will require to be part of the solution for generations to come. Be in it for the long haul because these families will enrich your life more than you'll ever know. Don't give up on them. They're worth it.

Sincerely,

Liz Lawryk

Gift Ideas for Teens and Adults!

A gift certificate for a massage!
(Do this inexpensively by contacting a licensed massage therapy college for student masseuse rates)

A gym pass and a session with a trainer

A scrapbook of events in their life

A yoga class with a friend

A bottle of body lotion, soaps in pleasing scents, bubble bath

A gel eye-pack, night eye-mask, ear plugs

A disc player, headset and a book or relaxation CD

A sampler of herbal teas and a pretty teacup or pottery mug

A makeup lesson
(Take her to a makeup counter and have a professional show how to properly use products - it's free!)

A camera and photo album

A new cool baseball cap, sunhat, sweatshirt with a hood or sunglasses *(To help filter the light)*

A bracelet, energy stone or worry beads
(So they have something nice to fidget with)

A lava lamp

A Dictaphone

A virtual fish tank for their bedroom

Egyptian cotton sheets

A hug

References

Badry, D., Lawryk, L. Editors. (2000). Letters to Our Children, Letters from Our Children: Living with Fetal Alcohol Syndrome and Related Effects. 109-110. Edmonton, Alberta, Canada. Alberta Association for Community Living.

Barth, R.P., Freundlich, M., Brodzinsky, D. Editors. (2000). Adoption and Prenatal Alcohol and Drug Exposure - Research, Policy, and Practice. Washington, D.C.,U.S.A. The Evan B. Donaldson Adoption Institute. Child Welfare League of America Inc.

Berg, S., Kinsey, K., Lutke, J., Wheway, D. (1997). FAS/E and Education: The Art of Making a Difference. British Columbia, Canada. FAS/E Support Network of B.C. Canada. Canada's Drug Strategy.

Bowlby, J. (1951). Maternal care and mental health. Geneva, World Health Organization: London: Her Majesty's Stationary Office; New York: Columbia University Press. Abridged version: Child care and the growth of love (2nd edition, 1965) Harmondsworth: Penguin.

Breen, J. (2000). Creating Vocational Success for Adults with Fetal Alcohol Syndrome - The Yukon Experience. Whitehorse, Yukon, Canada. Muttart Foundation.

Brick, J. Editor. (2004). Handbook of the Medical Consequences of Alcohol and Drug Abuse. Binghamton, New York, U.S.A. Haworth Press.

Buxton, B. (2004) Damaged Angels - A mother discovers the terrible cost of alcohol in pregnancy. Toronto, Ontario, Canada. A. Knopf.

Chudley, A. E., Conry, J., Cook, J. L., Looke, C., Rosales, T., LeBlanc, N. (2005). Fetal Alcohol Spectrum Disorder: Canadian Guidelines for diagnosis. Canadian Medical Association Journal CMAJ 2005; 172 (5 suppl): S1-S21. S20-S21.CMA Media Inc. (or it's licensors.)

Clarren, S.K. (1981) Recognition of the Fetal Alcohol Syndrome, JAMA; 245(23) 2436-2439

Coloroso, B. (1994) Kids are worth it! Giving Your Child The Gift Of Inner Discipline. Toronto, Ontario, Canada. Penguin.

Conry, J., Fast, D.K. (2000). Fetal Alcohol Syndrome and the Criminal Justice System. British Columbia Fetal Alcohol Syndrome Resource Society Vancouver. Maple Ridge, British Columbia. The Law Foundation of British Columbia, Canada.

Cook, P., Kellie, R., Jones, C., Goossen, L. (2000). Tough Kids And Substance Abuse - a drug awareness program for children and adolescents with ARND, FAS, FAE and cognitive disabilities. AFM Winnipeg, Manitoba, Canada. Manitoba Community Services Counsel Inc., Addictions Foundation of Manitoba, West Region Child and Family Services, Winnipeg School Division No.1. First Edition.

Davis, D. (1994) Reaching Out To Children with FAS/FAE - A Handbook for Teachers, Counselors, and Parents Who Work with Children Affected by Fetal Alcohol Syndrome and Fetal Alcohol Effects. West Nyack, NewYork, U.S.A. The Center for Applied Research In Education, A Simon and Schuster Company.

Dorris, M. (1989). The Broken Cord. New York, U.S.A. Harper Collins Publishers.

Edelstein, S. B. (1995). Children with Prenatal Alcohol

and/or Other Drug Exposure: Weighing The Risks Of Adoption. Washington, D.C., U.S.A. Child Welfare League of America Inc.

Falkner, L. (2002). I Would be Loved. College Station, Texas, U.S.A. Virtualbookworm.com Publishing Inc.

Froehlich, E., Robinson, M.J., Spack, C., Tozeland, J. (2003). Tips - Thoughts, Ideas, Practices and Strategies For Working Effectively with Children Who Have Alcohol Related Disorders: Second edition. A Handbook for Teachers and School Clinicians. Winnipeg, Manitoba, Canada. Guidance Clinic.

Graefe, S. Editor. (1998). FAS: Parenting Children Affected by Fetal Alcohol Syndrome. A Guide for Daily Living. 2nd edition revised. Vancouver, British Columbia. Society of Special Needs Adoptive Parents (SNAP), Adoption Counsel of Canada.

George, A. (1993). Guide for Parents, Teachers and Others Caring for Children with FAS/FAE and NAS. Vancouver, British Columbia, Canada. Vancouver YWCA.

Health Canada. (2004). Helping Families - Helping Children. A companion guide to the video Helping Families - Helping Children. Yellowknife, North West Territories, Canada. Yellowknife Association for Community Living.

James Bellis, T. (2003). When The Brain Can't Hear. Unraveling the mystery of Auditory Processing Disorder. New York, New York, U.S.A. Atria Books.

Kleinfeld, J., Westcott, S. (1993). Fantastic Antone Succeeds! Experiences in Educating Children with Fetal Alcohol Syndrome. Alaska, USA. University of Alaska Press.

Lawryk, L. (2004). Diagnostic Interpretation of Abilities Sessions. Bragg Creek, Alberta, Canada. OBD Triage Institute.

Lawryk, L. (1998). The OBD Triage Assessment Instrument and Model: A Screening Instrument for use in the Medical Evaluation of Teratogenic Effects on Embryonic Development. Bragg Creek, Alberta, Canada. OBD Triage Institute.

Mayer, L. Editor. (1998). Living And Working With Fetal Alcohol Syndrome / Effects. Winnipeg, Manitoba, Canada. Interagency FAS/E Program.

Michaud, M. A., Michaud, S. K. (2003). Beautiful Smiles, Gentle Spirits. Fetal Alcohol Spectrum Disorder: A Misunderstood Problem. Calgary, Alberta, Canada. Detselig Enterprises.

Niebuhr, R. (1932). The Serenity Prayer. Adapted in 1939 by Alcoholics Anonymous (r). Twelve Steps and Twelve Traditions. Alcoholics Anonymous World Services, Inc. Copyright (c) 1952, 1953, 1981 by the A.A. Grapevine, Inc., and Alcoholics Anonymous Publishing (Alcoholics Anonymous World Services. All rights reserved.

Normand, C., Rutman, L. D. (1996). Caring for Children with Fetal Alcohol Syndrome. Victoria, British Columbia, Canada. Child & Community Research Program School of Social Work, University of Victoria.

Page, K. (2003). The Invisible Havoc of Prenatal Alcohol Damage. 67-88. San Francisco, California. Journal of the Center For Families, Children and the Courts. Internet Source.

Pearce, J.W., Pezzot-Pearce, T.D. (1994). Attachment theory and its implications for psychotherapy with maltreated children. 18, 425-438. Child Abuse and Neglect.

Pearce, J.W., Pezzot-Pearce, T.D. (1997). Psychotherapy of Abused and Neglected Children. New York, N.Y., U.S.A. Guilford Press.

Ruiz, M. D. (1997). The Four Agreements. San Rafael, California, U.S.A. Amber-Allen Publishing, Inc. Reprinted by permission.

Rutman, D. La ,Berge, C., Wheway, D. (2005). Parenting with FASD - Challenges, Strategies and Supports. Victoria, British Columbia, Canada. A partnership of the School of Social Work, University of Victoria and the FAS/E Support Network of British Columbia, Canada.

Sears, W., Thompson, L. (1998). The A.D.D. Book. New Understandings, New Approaches to Parenting Your Child. Boston, New York, U.S.A. Little, Brown and Company Publishing.

Stock Kranowitz, C. (1998). The Out-of-Sync Child - Recognizing and Coping with Sensory Integration Dysfunction. New York, New York, U.S.A. Skylight Press. A Pedigree Book.The Berkley Publishing Group.

Streissguth, A.P., Barr, H.M., Kogan, J., Bookstein, F.L. (1996) Understanding the occurance of secondary disabilities of clients with fetal alcohol syndrome and fetal alcohol effect: final report. Washington, D.C., U.S.A. Presented on Fetal Alcohol Syndrome Conference in Washington, D.C., U.S.A.

Streissguth, A.P. (1997). Fetal Alcohol Syndrome - A Guide for Families and Communities. Baltimore, Maryland, U.S.A. Paul H. Brooks Publishing Co.

Streissguth, A.P., Kanter, J. Editors. (1997). The Challenge of Fetal Alcohol Syndrome - Overcoming Secondary Disabilities. Washington, U.S.A. University of Washington Press.

Strong, J. Flanagan, M. (2005). AD/HD for Dummies. Indianapolis, Indiana, U.S.A. Wiley Publishing Inc.

Umansky, W., Steinberg Smalley, B. (2003). ADHD - Helping Your Child: A Comprehensive Program To Treat Attention Deficit /Hyperactivity Disorders At Home And In School. Boston, Massachusetts, U.S.A. Warner Books.

Weschler, D. (1981). Wechsler Intelligence Scales for Children Third Edition - Revised (WISC-III-R), San Antonio, Texas, U.S.A. The Psychological Corporation. Harcourt Brace and Company.

Weschler, D. (1981). Wechsler Intelligence Achievement Test for Children (WIAT). San Antonio, Texas, U.S.A. The Psychological Corporation. Harcourt Brace and Company.

Other Sources

A League of Their Own. (1992). (Film). Marshall, P. Director. U.S.A. Columbia Tristar.

FAS Forward: A Fresh Look at Fetal Alcohol Syndrome. (2002). (Video.) Calgary, Alberta, Canada. BPN 5071701. Mount Royal College and Access Distribution (1-888-440-4640).

Index

Did you borrow this book?

If you would like to own a copy for yourself,
or to give to someone else,
go to www.obdtriage.com to order.